Diana

FOR GIRLS

—printed and published
by
D.C. Thomson & Co. Ltd.,
Dundee and London.

A
B
B
A

DOUBLE TROUBLE FOR
SAMANTHA

NINETEEN *year-old Samantha Taylor had decided to take the plunge, and was off, on her own, for a two week holiday in sunny Ibiza . . .*

Look after yourself, love!

I will, Mum! Don't worry! Bye! Bye, Dad!

At the bus station . . .

YOUNG SCENE TOURS

Young Scene Tours! That's the one! Ibiza here I come!

12

'Ere we are, boys! New partners for you. You will wait till ladies change, yes?

You bet!

I'ave ze announcement to make. New holidaymakers 'ave arrived. We'll give zem ze big welcome and include zem in ze tournament.

She's a bit of all right!

Hands off! I saw her first!

But more double trouble for Sam was looming on her Ibizan horizon!

They soon forgot about me! Oh, well—at least I'll get some peace now! I'll go and write a few postcards.

Hi! I'm Ken—I've just arrived.

So have I. I'm Rick.

How about going to the disco with me tonight?

I asked her first, knucklehead!

Seems like I'm going to have to wait till I get back to Scunthorpe to enjoy the quiet life again!

GET INTO GEAR ~ FOR
GHOST HUNTING

MOST girls enjoy telling ghost stories round a flickering fire with friends, scaring each other half to death. But what would happen if you actually came face to face with a ghost? Would you bravely stop and talk to it, or would you take to your heels and run?

" Diana " girl, Angela Shaw, from Lower Kersal in Lancashire, wrote to us saying that there was nothing she would like more, than to go on a ghost-hunting expedition!

" And, right on my doorstep is Kersal Cell, a Country Club, which is supposed to be absolutely teeming with ghosts." Angela added.

First of all we had to go on our own special fashion hunt for clothes to go ghost-hunting in! And, after several hours of turning the Manchester branches of C & A and Littlewoods, upside down, we arrived at Kersal Cell, armed with enough clothes to disarm twenty ghosts, if necessary!

Before daring to venture inside, Angela donned a C & A, Sixth Sense, green boucle knitted skirt and matching tunic with hood.

" If any ghosts are lurking around, this is a good disguise because they won't be able to see me against the grass and trees." She laughed.

Next came an outfit, also from C & A, consisting of brown, cord trousers, green rolled-collared sweater and tweed hacking jacket. And, to crown the lot, a fashionable flat cap.

" When Henry VIII suppressed the monasteries, the Kenyon family bought Kersal Cell and lived in it for four generations." Angela informed me. " Perhaps, when the daughters rode across the fields on their horses, they were dressed something like I am now. Who knows?"

Who knows indeed! But one thing we didn't know was what terrors awaited us inside.

So to be prepared for her first spook, Angela dressed in blue denim jeans, a red and navy check lumber-jack shirt, with a perky page-boy hat from Littlewoods.

"This is a bold outfit which gives me the courage I need to go inside." She gave a mock shudder.

After the Restoration, Kersal Cell was sold to Edward Byrom, whose son, John, wrote the world-famous carol "Christians Awake".

Peering round the door of what was once John Byrom's bedroom, Angela shivered in anticipation.

"If anywhere is haunted, it must be this room." She told me, holding up her next beautiful outfit—a long orange and white dress (C & A) with one hand and clutching a candle-stick in the other.

Next door to John Byrom's bedroom is the Chapel, with its hidden priest hole where, it is said, the monks used to gather for their daily prayers.

"This is even more eerie." Angela whispered. "I might be fourteen but I could do with my old Teddy for company."

For a quick get-away, from any ghost who just might be lurking about, Angela could think of nothing better than a colourful striped woollen top with matching leg-warmers.

"If I see the hooded monk who they say walks up here, I can whizz down this old Jacobean bannister and be out of the place in no time," she claimed.

In recent years, many people visiting Kersal Cell, have told of hearing doors creak or slam of their own accord. An unseen bell tolls and, in the height of summer, rooms suddenly freeze for no apparent reason.

"I've heard that a lady dressed in grey, can be heard weeping for her dead child in this room." Angela told me, walking into what was once the family sitting-room.

By this time she was wearing a red pinafore dress with a yellow blouse to match the trimmings. (Littlewoods)

" Listen, can you hear something?"

I was pleased to say I couldn't hear a thing and, before you could say " there's a ghost creeping up behind you", Angela had changed into a short sleeved navy Cat-suit, with a red polo-necked blouse. (C & A)—enough to disarm any ghost.

In the Sundial Room, named because of its unusual outdoor brass sundial over the fireplace, Angela picked up an iron black cat from the fireplace.

" What an evil-looking cat. They say black cats are supposed to be lucky but this one scares me," she shuddered.

A little later, in the same room, wearing a navy skirt, with a pretty laced, flowered belt and pink cheesecloth blouse (Littlewoods), Angela pointed out that it was here, that John Byrom wrote " Christians Awake."

" He wrote the carol as a Christmas present for his daughter, Dolly in 1747. And, did you know that it was John Byrom who invented the first modern shorthand system?"

Bonnie Prince Charlie was supposed to have stopped off at Kersal Cell on his march to Derby and, it is for this reason that a beautiful oak-panelled room, now a dining-room, was named after him.

" Isn't this dress absolutely gorgeous?" Angela danced into the room, her brown eyes shining with excitement wearing a lovely white, chiffon dress, (C & A) much bonnier, I'm sure, than the ill-fated Prince Charlie.

" In the fireplace there is supposed to be a secret passage which leads to the Cathedral in Manchester," Angela remembered, peeping into it.

" Oooh . . . . .Do you know it's gone quite cold in this room, all of a sudden. They say it does go cold when a ghost is around don't they?

" And, do you think it's my imagination or can I really hear scratching sounds coming from inside that chimney. Er—time we were going, I reckon."

And so, off went Angela to tell her friends, Mandy, Diane and Elisa, all about her ghostly but fashionable adventures on her fourteenth birthday at Kersal Hall!

by JANE McFIE

IT HAPPENED ON A MOONLIGHT CLEAR

A CHRISTMAS STORY by VALERIE EDWARDS

I WAS really thrilled to bits when the St John's Carollers asked me to join their choir. We'd only just moved to the little Wiltshire village—at the beginning of December actually—and we'd hardly got to know a soul.

Oh, they were kind enough, all of them, but being so near Christmas they had so much to do it was difficult to spare time for newcomers.

And then, out of the blue, I got this invitation.

I couldn't imagine anything nicer than going out singing carols on Christmas Eve. I hoped it would snow, and on the night of the twenty-third, it did.

We were in for a beautiful, traditional white Christmas.

"Wrap up warm now," Mum said.

I wound my scarf round my neck over my cosy red anorak and went out into the black night.

At St John's, we were each given one of those old-fashioned brass oil-lamps.

We looked an odd band as we set off, just our pale faces visible in the flickering orange glow. Being the newest member, and really not with that good a voice, I kept well to the rear.

IT had been decided to visit all the big houses on the outskirts of the village that Christmas Eve, and to sing to the villagers themselves on the common on Christmas morning.

As we left the lights of the village behind, and began to skirt the woods and fields that lay beyond, I moved closer to the line in front of me.

At the first house we came to we were given fruit punch and hot mince-pies. Super. It really warmed me up. I was quite happy to trudge on after that.

I was swinging my lamp and watching the patterns it made in the snow when I saw the next place loom up. It stood on the very top of the hill, a great square box of a place.

Victorian, I thought to myself. We were doing Victorian architecture at school. I was so interested in gazing at it that I didn't realise the other singers had filed past the heavy, ornate metalwork gate without giving it a second glance.

I was just about, regretfully, to do the same when a girl's voice suddenly called out to me: "Oh do please come in! Please!"

I only hesitated for a second. After all, I could easily catch the others up — I knew the next couple of houses quite well. And somehow . . . well, I wanted to go in. I can't explain why. It was just a feeling.

I PUSHED the gate open, and walked up the wide path.

The front door gave at my touch. I'd meant to ring the bell first, but I couldn't see one.

After a second or two, I hesitantly popped my head round the door.

The spluttering gas mantle from a bracket on the wall was the first thing that caught my eye. How quaint, I thought. It looks real, the genuine article, but it can't be. It must be a clever imitation. I took a step forward to get a closer view.

As I did so, the front door clanged shut behind me. It made me jump.

The draught caught at my oil lamp and the gas mantle and for a second they both went dim. Just for that moment, I had the oddest sensation I was in a tunnel of absolute darkness.

Then, the light came up again. I was able to see a curving staircase to the right of me, and, just descending it, a woman in a long scarlet dress, her dark hair piled high on top of her head.

She came down very slowly, as if deep in thought. She didn't even notice me, standing there in the flickering shadow.

As she passed me, I started to ask her if she would like me to sing, but she couldn't have heard because she walked straight on and into a room at the end of the passage.

I wasn't sure now what to do. Perhaps I'd imagined the girl who had called out to me. Perhaps that was why the rest of the carol singers hadn't stopped, because they knew they weren't welcome here.

THEN, as I stood there, the door opposite me opened, and a nurse rustled out carrying something on a tray.

She turned away from me and moved off in the direction the other woman had taken. As she disappeared, I heard the girl's voice again, calling to me from inside the room.

I pushed open the door and went in.

She was lying on a low bed near the window, covered by a dark blue counterpane. The pillows were built up high behind her head, and her long golden hair hung in two plaits in front of her shoulders. She was very pale, with two big circles of red on her cheekbones. She looked just about my own age.

"Hallo," she said. Her voice was very

breathless, as if she'd been running and had a job to get the words out. Sort of rasping. Then she coughed, and I realised she was very ill indeed. "Come nearer," she begged. "It's getting so dark, I can't see you clearly."

I thought that very odd because the room was brilliantly lit with those old-fashioned gas mantles standing just about everywhere.

I went forward, catching my knee painfully against a heavy mahogany sideboard.

Crikey, I thought, they might have a Victorian house but why on earth do they fill it with all this old stuff?

"Please . . . please sing for me," she said. "I haven't . . . haven't heard any carollers this year. Mama says I am too ill."

So that's the reason the others didn't stop, I thought. What a shame. Surely one song couldn't have hurt?

"'Course I will," I said cheerfully. I set my brass oil-lamp down on a little table, and took a deep breath.

Just as I was halfway through "Hark The Herald Angels Sing," the woman in the scarlet dress came in. She ignored me and went straight over to the bed.

"My little love," she said to the girl. "Why, you're smiling. That's the first time I've seen you smile for a long time, Eleanor."

"It's her," the girl said, pointing at me. "She sings so beautifully, Mama. It makes me so very happy."

A frightened look crossed the woman's face. She stared past me, her eyes brimming with tears.

I faltered in my singing, but only Eleanor seemed to notice.

"Oh please . . . please don't stop!" she begged. "I wish . . . I wish I could join you . . ."

Then as if the effort of talking were too much for her, she dropped her head back on the pillows.

Her mother gave a loud cry, and the nurse rushed in. They both bent over Eleanor.

I really shouldn't have come, I thought suddenly. I'd better go before they bawl me out.

I TIPTOED to the door and let myself out.

It wasn't until I was halfway to the next house that I remembered I'd left my oil-lamp behind.

I turned back and had covered quite a stretch when I heard voices and hurrying footsteps behind me.

"There she be!" said the leading caroller. "We bin a-looking everywhere for you, lass. Thought you'd bin and got yourself lost."

"I stopped at the house up there," I said. "On the hill. The girl there seemed terribly ill. Then I went and left my oil-lamp behind."

"There bain't no house on the hill," said one of the older singers, a bent grey-haired little man.

"'Twas once, though, long ago. Squire lived there. I were nobbut a tiny shaver at the time, no more'n three year old. 'Course I knew nothing about it at the time like, but I heard the tale many a time since.

"Squire's daughter were taken ill with the fever and her died on the Christmas Eve. Died with a smile on her lips they said, listening to an angel singing. That's what she said with her last dying breath, poor girl. 'Mama, I hear an angel singing '."

I felt a cold shiver touch my spine. Then I shook myself. It was ridiculous, I'd been in the house, hadn't I? I'd even left my oil lamp there.

I smiled at the carol singer, while the others clustered round, saying nothing.

"We're talking about different places," I said cheerfully. "I'll just collect my oil lamp, shan't be a mo'."

They stood and watched as I hurried the last few yards.

I rounded the corner.

The top of the hill lay covered in a thick coat of white snow which was still falling in large brittle flakes.

Very faintly I could still see the prints of our shoes as we trudged past. There were the indistinct outlines of a set going away from the rest. Towards . . . where?

Of the house I'd been in there was no sign, just a line of bleak, leafless trees, the cold wind murmuring and calling through them. Like the faint voice of a very ill, breathless young girl . . . ●

Sixpence for a
broken heart

PRETTY eighteen-year-old Pam Stewart from London had just been proclaimed Beauty Queen of Seaford. But her dazzling smile hid her true feelings . . .

Pam's photographer boyfriend, Paul, was in the crowd.

Pam's lovely, but I wish she didn't have to do this for a living.

Later—

But her mum's not well, and Pam needs the money.

Later, in a coffee bar—

How I hate these beauty contests, Paul! It's all Dad's fault! He left Mum and me five years ago when we lived in Australia. Then Mum took ill—she was heart-broken. At least the beauty contests give me time to look after her.

Must go, Paul—Mum will need me. See you tomorrow.

Poor Pam—she has a hard life. And she's so proud! I want to marry her, but she says she couldn't burden me with her invalid mother. But I would put up with anything for her . . .

At home—

Hello, Mum. How are you?

As if you care! Where have you been, Pam?

23

Number four's name? Pam Stewart—

That name . . . I wish I could remember!

The contest ended, with Pam the easy winner.

Pam Stewart—Miss Beachton.

As Pam left the stage—

Excuse me . . . Miss Stewart . . .

Sorry, I'm tired. I don't feel like talking.

But I must speak to you—it's very important!

Push off, buster—she said she was tired!

The stranger found out Pam's address and—at the nearest phone box—

Could she be? I must find out!

I'll see if I can arrange a meeting with her. I know . . .

So—

Oh, my head! That phone!

I'll get it, Mum.

''RING''

24

You'll think this is very sudden, but I saw you today at the beauty contest, and I want to offer you a job modelling in my store—

Well, I don't know . . .

Meet me tomorrow. Martine's—three o'clock. We'll discuss it then.

I—okay, then.

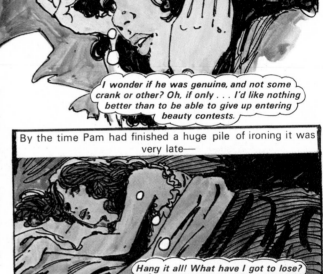

Later that night, Pam began to think about the offer—

I wonder if he was genuine, and not some crank or other? Oh, if only . . . I'd like nothing better than to be able to give up entering beauty contests.

Who was that, Pam? My head aches so.

Just a friend, Mum—nothing for you to worry about. I'll get you a couple of your headache pills.

I wonder who that was? Anyway, I'm not meeting him. I only said I would to get rid of him!

By the time Pam had finished a huge pile of ironing it was very late—

Hang it all! What have I got to lose? I WILL meet him.

So, next day, at three o'clock sharp—

I'm so glad you've come, Miss Stewart. You'll see that my offer of work is quite genuine . . .

Good—she doesn't recognise me!

The man's voice broke off as he stared at Pam's unusual necklace.

I . . . where did you get that necklace—that half sixpence?

I—I've had it for years! I don't know where it came from.

The cut off picture of Dad! Poor Mum—she doesn't hate Dad after all! She must hope he'll come back some day. But I hate him for making Mum so unhappy!

Next day, Pam began her new job.

Pam's a lovely girl and she's doing well on her first day, but I must bide my time, not get too impatient.

A happy carefree month passed for Pam, then—

Pam soon found out.

You're doing very well, that's why. I always reward hard work.

Why—my salary is even more than Mr Smith said! I wonder why?

He's a really nice man. He knows I've got Mum to look after.

At home—

Hello, dear. Did you have a good day? Mrs Perkins has only just left. The stew is on, and I peeled the potatoes for you.

Mum is much perkier these days.

And later—

And she gets on really well with Paul now. Life is rosy thanks to Mr Smith.

As Paul left—

I love you, Pam—let's get married. Your mum could live with us.

Oh, Paul—it wouldn't be fair on you. I'm sorry.

A few days later—

Ah, Pam. Er—I'd like a word with you in my office, if you don't mind.

It's about this, Pam—

The other half-sixpence! Where did you get that?

Like you, Pam—I've always had it. You see—I'm your father!

What? But you can't be! He's in Australia! He left Mum and me—

AUGUST 6

I admit I've changed quite a bit, but I can explain that.

You ruined my mother's life! I hate you for that! I never want to see you again!

Wait, Pam! I can explain!

I must see Paul! He'll be off duty just now.

Pam found comfort in Paul's arms—

Oh, Paul! Oh, Paul!

It's okay, Pam—don't cry.

I—I'll just have to go back to the beauty contests! I'll give up my job in the store!

Later—

I've left the store. I can't say why, Mum. Mrs Perkins will have to go, and I'll start the beauty contests again.

But why—?

Pam rushed off sobbing—

Oh, I feel so miserable—but I mustn't let Mum know the reason I left the store!

Will Pam Stewart come to the judge's tent, please?

A few weeks later, after many urgent phone calls from Mr Smith, which Pam ignored—

The judging will be over soon, and I can go home to see to Mum. I—I hope Mr Smith doesn't phone again. Mum's got steadily worse since I left the store—

What's happened? Maybe it's Mum!

A heart attack, I'm afraid. Something has been distressing him, I'd say.

Mr Smith of Smith's Stores has collapsed. He asked for you before he became unconscious.

Oh, no! What happened?

And I know what! It's all my fault. Oh, I hope he'll be all right.

I'll just go and get dressed, then I'll come to the hospital with you.

At the hospital—

He's still unconscious, I'm afraid!

Poor Dad. Dad! That's the first time I've thought of him as that—my dad!

Eyes flickered open—

It—it's you, Pam!

Don't talk—just get better.

And a few days later—

You must let me explain, Pam. I didn't leave you and your mother five years ago—I was knocked down by a hit-and-run driver. When I came to I'd lost my memory, and I had no identification on me—

Oh, poor Dad . . .

TEMPERATURE CHART

I wandered around aimlessly, but I couldn't remember anything. I began to build a new life for myself. Then I started to remember little things . . .

After a long time I realised I had a family somewhere—something prompted me to return to England—I felt sure I'd find my family there. I became a successful business man. Then I saw you . . . and something clicked into place.

And I know the rest.

But will your mother believe me, Pam?

I think she'll welcome you back with open arms, Dad. I'm sure she still loves you.

30

JANIE

PART ONE

by VALERIE EDWARDS

"LADIES and gentlemen— Spinning Jenny!"

Janie held her breath and pressed closer to the edge of the stage as the curtains folded back and the three-boy group began to play.

Dark-haired Rich on the drums looked in her direction and grinned; they'd all seen Janie many times. She always tried to turn up, wherever they appeared. Now she began swaying to the music, her eyes closed.

Any minute now the pretty blonde-haired girl singer would appear, and go into the opening number. Janie knew it off by heart, she'd practised all their numbers over and over to herself, standing in front of her dressing-table mirror.

But the act went on, and the singer didn't appear.

The disco audience began to get restless. They were used to vocals on record or live, and it was obvious they didn't think they were getting their money's value.

When the curtains closed after the first half, there were several discontented boos. The queue for autographs at the stage door was the smallest Janie had ever seen.

What could have happened to their singer?

Almost without conscious thought, she found herself pushing the bar and going into the dimly-lit passage.

Rich was just coming out of one of the tiny, bare dressing-rooms and he stopped when he saw her and said: " Thought you'd had enough autographs from us, love."

" I just wondered what had happened to Pearl," she said, all in a rush.

" You and the rest of the crowd," he said. " She's left us flat and it looks as if it's just about going to finish us, doesn't it? First time on tonight without her, and look at the reception. Hardly worth going on second half."

" Oh, but you must!" Janie cried.

" Wouldn't like to step in would you?" he said jokingly. He pushed open the door of the dressing-room and Janie followed him in. The other two in the group were sat on the floor, playing cards.

" Do you really mean it?" Janie breathed.

Rich stared at her.

" I was only joking, kid. Can't sing, can you?"

Only every number you do, Janie thought. Aloud she said: " Yes, a bit."

Les picked up his guitar and began strumming, very softly. It was one of Janie's favourites, and she couldn't stop herself joining in. The two of them finished it right through to the end.

" Say, that's pretty good." Les looked across at Andy, who played bass. " What think, Andy?"

" We've nothing to lose I guess." Andy stood up and stretched. " Try her out on one or two more. We might introduce her, gradually." He looked reflectively at Janie. " Her gear's okay, anyway. Couldn't mistake her for Pearl, but that might be a good thing."

It seemed like a dream to Janie. Any minute someone was going to pinch her and she'd wake up and she'd be back on the wrong side of the stage again . . . wishing and wondering and hoping . . .

But it was real enough.

"Just two in the second half" Andy said briefly. " Opening and end. Like you've just run through. Right?"

The marvellous part of it was that she didn't feel a bit nervous. Somehow it felt as if she'd been doing it all her life. The fans didn't boo this time, and she could see the boys were pleased.

" Welcome to Spinning Jenny," Rich said. " Go over the paperwork later. Meanwhile, we'll pack up, collect our cash and get out of here. Give us a hand, will you?"

Willingly Janie helped them with their instruments, packing them into the ramshackle old van. By the time they'd finished, the hall was in darkness, and only the dim lights of the stage showed.

" Where's the manager?" Andy asked the tired old doorman, who was already dozing off in a corner.

He waved a hand in the direction of the back of the hall.

" Gone," he said. " It was his last night. Moving on or something. Left this for you." He handed Andy an envelope.

Andy ripped it open, took out the five pound note it contained, and whistled angrily through his teeth.

" We've been rooked again," he said grimly. " That's the second time in a month we haven't been paid our fee. And this is hardly enough to pay for the petrol to our next gig. What on earth are we going to do?"

This six-part story continues throughout your Diana Book.

CHARLOTTE HOLMES 'N' WATSON

IT all began one autumn evening at 21a Baker Avenue, home of Charlotte Holmes—but let Charlotte tell you, she's quite a story teller and quite a girl.

And it's a real mystery who Billy Bingley is asking to the office Christmas dance! I reckon it should be me—but then I'm biased. That's him out there, by the way.

Hi! Excuse the magnifying glass in the picture above, but I've got to keep up my image. They say I'm a direct descendant of the famous detective Sherlock Holmes, you know! I certainly have this constant urge to solve mysteries with my colleague, Watson.

...to land very neatly in Billy's cup of coffee.

GERROUTOFIT!

Who on earth caused that commotion? So much for my second act for the office Xmas Revue.

With a face as red as an apple, Charlotte slunk off.

Oops! My mistake. Now how did it go—I love you my darling . . . and whoever is writing the captions out there, let's have less of the "Apple Charlotte" funnies, OK!

Later at home—

My jealous heart! Billy was only writing a play. Ah, well—the paths of true sleuths seldom run smoothly. By the way—Watson, my undercover partner got a good wigging from me! It was his fault—he tripped over that blinking cat.

Next night at a disco.

Billy's here tonight—and I've got a fresh plan! Watch carefully. Now you see me—

36

spare time pop stars

LEIF GARRETT

" Something speedy! I used to love skateboarding, but when I bought my car I decided that skateboards were much too slow for me! I've bought myself a Fiat 124 Sports Spider Convertible—that's what I call speedy!"

ALAN SILSON (SMOKIE)

" Whenever I've got any spare time and money I go out and buy old guitars, take them to pieces and then put them back together again. I even do this with new ones, because I find I can alter the sound of them to my liking. Obviously it takes some time but it makes a definite improvement."

RAY LAKE (REAL THING)

" I ride my motorbike. I never had a bike until about a year ago. A mate of mine took me up to North Wales and let me drive his up and down the mountains and through the streams. I thought it was terrific.
" That was the first time I'd ever ridden one of my own, and then when he went away he let me borrow it. Eventually I bought myself a beautiful big Triumph 750. Now all my spare time is spent on it."

RAY STILES (MUD)

" I'm a photography fanatic. Ever since Mud began I've carried a camera with me and I've kept scrapbooks on everything we've done, but now I'm doing it a bit more seriously.
" I've got quite a collection of cameras, but I tend to use my Pentax most. My favourite subjects are people and kids; I'm not over keen on landscapes. Also I've recently started developing my own films, but I still prefer the actual taking of the photos."

ANDY GIBB

" Sports of any kind. I've done virtually everything; parachuting, skin-diving, motorbike racing, fishing, flying.
" Obviously I've had some hair-raising experiences at times, but nothing bad enough to stop me having another go."

JAMIE STONE (FLINTLOCK)

" Before I started taking up music seriously I used to do a lot of cycling. I had a couple of friends who were cycling fanatics too. Every week we used to ride to Aybridge near Haynock Forrest and ride around the aerodrome.
" I don't get too much time for that now, but occasionally I look out on a sunny day and fancy a trip somewhere in the country."

EDDY AMOO (REAL THING)

" I've got two big hobbies—one's watching Liverpool football team playing a match and the other's playing chess. I've been playing for a couple of years now, and I'm totally addicted, but I've got a big problem—trying to find an opponent.
" None of the other guys in the band can play and none of them is interested in learning, so I can't play as often as I'd like to."

MIKE HOLLOWAY (FLINTLOCK)

" Besides drumming the rest of my spare time is spent making wooden aeroplanes. I usually make them from balsa wood because it's strong but very light.
" When I've finished one I generally end up smashing it when I take it out on its first flight!"

LIP READING!

DIANA BEAUTY FEATURE

THE shape and expression of a mouth tell such a lot about a girl—whether she's cheerful or gloomy, timid or bold, stingy or generous, fun, or a wee bit dull. See if your own lips are shown in our Lips Character Guide, and if so, do you like what you find? If you don't, there's still plenty you can do about it!

MERRY MOUTH.

THIS mouth turns up at the corners, brightens the whole face. Shows: optimism, sense of humour, ability to make the best of things. The owner of such a mouth tends to be popular and have many friends.

Beauty hint: emphasize this pleasing mouth with lip gloss in pink, red or natural.

GLOOMY MOUTH.

THIS mouth turns down on all but the rarest occasions and is often seen in an otherwise pretty face. Shows: a tendency to self-pity and general discontent, even when things go well.

Beauty hint: make a list of seven good things in your life and look at it each time you catch a down-in-the-mouth reflection. Try smiling a lot! It won't hurt!

THIN LIPS.

THIN lips are said to show meanness, though more often this is skill at handling money matters. You are capable of exceptional kindness to those in need and have a strong sense of right and wrong.

Beauty hint: light, bright lip colours give good results. Extend lip outline slightly with lip liner pencil or lip brush. (See dotted line)

FULL LIPS.

THIS mouth may be a little larger than you would like. Shows: generosity and a very likeable nature. Fun to be with, that's you.

Beauty hint: a neater shape is given if shape of mouth is outlined just within the lips by lip pencil, then filled in with a natural or darkish lipstick. Avoid bright colours. (See dotted line)

JUTTING LOWER LIP.

LOWER lip sticks out, shows one with strong likes and dislikes. Found in masterful types with great ability. Can also show aggression and obstinacy. Tendency to choose friends with softer personalities.

Beauty tip: use two different shades of lipstick, a darker tone to 'reduce' the lower lip, a lighter one to highlight upper lip. Blend carefully.

RECEDING LOWER LIP.

SHOWS a sensitive nature, possibly artistic. One who has many fears in life, often without cause.

Beauty hint: cultivate a more positive attitude. You'll feel and look braver. Using two lipsticks, give emphasis to small lower lip with highlights and 'reduce' overlapping upper lip with darker colour. Blend carefully.

SULKY MOUTH.

SHOWS someone who feels sorry for herself a lot of the time, often without justification. Can lead to permanent lines of discontent around the mouth if not checked.

Beauty hint: check often in a mirror that your expression wouldn't turn the milk sour!

TENSE MOUTH.

THIS mouth, tight and unrelaxed, reflects a tension often echoed in the eyes. Shows: a worrier—about exams, about friendships, about anything and everything!

Beauty hint: fresh air, exercise, sensible food, a good hobby and enough sleep should make you and your mouth more relaxed. A really shiny lip gloss will give a softer effect.

SNEERING LIPS.

SPOIL the entire facial expression. Show one who believes she knows best and looks down on nearly everybody and everything. Friends hard to get, harder to keep.

Beauty hint: take a good look at your attitude, then at those sneering lips and try to change both!

TREMBLING LIPS.

YOU are easily moved to tears or laughter and your mouth shows every emotion—tears, giggles, the lot. You are a good friend and capable of great affection.

Beauty hint: try a firm lip outline with lip crayon, blending in your favourite lipstick shade.

PARTED LIPS.

PARTED when in repose, these lips often belong to someone thoughtful, even a bit of a dreamer. A good listener, people like to confide in you.

Beauty hint: your teeth show a lot and merit brushing morning, noon and night.

STERN (OR POKER) MOUTH.

YOU have deep feelings which you are skilled at concealing, and this has been known to discourage would-be friends who find you a little formidable. You are utterly reliable.

Beauty hint: a smile now and then would lighten your expression, and make your face more interesting. Lip gloss will give softer lip curves.

SMALL, "PRISSY" MOUTH.

YOU are skilled at anything which calls for persistence and concentration, both in your work and the arts, although your manner is a little too intense at times.

Beauty hint: paint an outline with a lip brush, slightly beyond normal lip line, to make mouth look more generous. (See dotted line)

POUTING MOUTH.

THIS may have charmed when you were knee-high to a grasshopper, but now it only shows a petulant manner which will become positively disagreeable with age!

Beauty hint: avoid pursing lips, or drawing mouth down to one side. Think cheerfully.

PLACID MOUTH OR PERFECT MOUTH.

THIS mouth is calm with nearly always a hint of a smile. Shows a well-balanced girl, tactful with family and friends. Contented, she does well if circumstances call for change and adaptability.

Beauty hint: enhance the attractive lines of this mouth with pencil lipstick, or use your favourite gloss.

A WINTERY NIGHT. A COSY FIRE AND YOU...

Here are some puzzles just for you when you're snuggled up by a cosy fire on a wet, wintery night. You'll find the answers below—but no peeping!

1

CAN YOU IDENTIFY THE SILHOUETTES?

2

LOOK FOR THE LETTERS OF THE ALPHABET THAT ONLY APPEAR ONCE, THEN SEE IF YOU CAN MAKE THE MAN'S NAME FROM THEM.

3

WRITE DOWN THE NAME OF EACH OBJECT IN THE APPROPRIATE SPACE. THE FIRST LETTER FROM EACH WORD WILL MAKE ANOTHER OBJECT. WRITE THIS IN THE SPACE UNDER THE BLANK BOX AND ALSO DRAW THE OBJECT ABOVE.

4

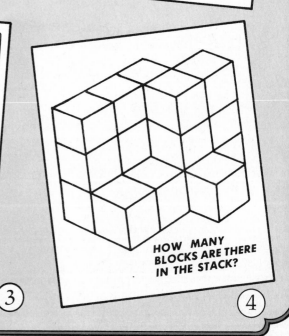

HOW MANY BLOCKS ARE THERE IN THE STACK?

5

IN THE JUMBLE OF LETTERS ARE FOUR THINGS YOU WOULD SEE AT THE CIRCUS. CAN YOU FIND THEM?

6

CAN YOU MAKE EIGHT, FOUR-LETTER WORDS FROM SPRING?

7

CAN YOU PAIR UP THE KEYS?

8

STUDY THE OBJECTS ABOVE, NOW COVER THEM AND SEE HOW MANY YOU CAN REMEMBER.

ANSWERS

1—KIWI, JUG, PALETTE, SCYTHE, MASK, BAT, SEA-HORSE, FISH, BIRD.
2—HORACE.
3—A. Butterfly, Apple, Talon. BAT.
  B. Hammer, Acorn, Top. HAT.
  C. Candle, Arrow, Peapod. CAP.
4—NUMBER OF BLOCKS—18.
5—CLOWN, RINGMASTER, STRONGMAN, ACROBAT.
6—GRIN, RING, SING, PING, SNIP, SPIN, GRIP, SIGN.
7—A and E, B and C, D and F, G and H.
8—SPINNING-TOP, RABBIT, AXE, FLOWER, STAR, BOW, CARROT, FISH, PEG, SEA-HORSE, SNAIL, TOADSTOOL, ENVELOPE.

The Name of the Game

HAVE you ever wondered how Pop groups choose their names and why they choose a particular one? We did a bit of scouting around and this is what we found.

THE ARTFUL DODGERS

AS you take a close look at this band you may think that three of them are brothers, but in fact only two of them are.

When they first started they were simply called THE DODGERS, but they discovered that there was another group around with the same name, so the ARTFUL bit came later. It was the character in the book 'Oliver Twist' that gave them the idea.

THE SPRINKLERS

IN 1977 this band, THE SPRINKLERS, appeared on and won "New Faces".

They later became Dennis Waterman's backing group. But shortly after this they got work as a band in their own right, so they had to find a suitable name for themselves.

Somebody came up with the suggestion THE SPRINKLERS, (Waterman! Sprinklers, get it?) but there's absolutely nothing wet about this group.

WINDOW

WINDOW are a five piece band. Apparently their name was chosen by the girl friend of the original singer, who's long since left them.

Although they don't consider

WINDOW to be a particularly original name, it's one that's used every day, and a lot of other words and ideas can easily come from it.

After all, it's pretty paneless (!) Also it's a smashing (!) word that you can quite easily latch (!) onto!

FLINTLOCK

ONE of the best known bands around, but do you know how they chose their name?

Young Mike Holloway says, "It was so difficult to know what to call ourselves. There were hundreds of suggestions —not always polite ones! But eventually we came up with a dozen of the strongest ones."

"We sent these names to

Roger Price, producer of our, "You Must Be Joking!" programme.

"It so happens that he's a gun fanatic and has a huge collection of them so the name FLINTLOCK was the choice."

BLONDIE

WHEN fair-haired, lead singer Debbie Harry used to walk around the streets people used to yell out 'Hey, Blondie'.

So the name just stuck with her, and when the band was formed it seemed like a good name for them because it's easy to remember. "Trouble is," remarks Debbie, "it means I can never change the colour of my hair again!"

JANIE

PART TWO

"GOOD of your people to put us up for a few nights, Janie," Rich said, as they drove along. " Saved our bacon and gave us time to catch up on rehearsals. How's it feel to be a fully-fledged and paid-up member of Spinning Jenny?"

" Great," said Janie enthusiastically. She sat hunched up on the front seat between Rich and Andy, hugging her knees and watching the grey road unfold in front of them. She couldn't wait to reach the hall in the next big town.

" Been trying to get an audition lined up with a record company." Les spoke from the depths of the van, surrounded by instruments. " Bit like winning the pools. How much further, Andy?"

" Another forty at least. Coming on to rain, too. Watch out for the next signpost."

They hit a bump, and Janie lost her balance. Rich slipped an arm round her shoulders.

" Here steady on," he said. " Can't lose you now!"

" You mean you can't," grinned Andy, and Janie blushed scarlet. " Hey, that matches your blouse," Andy added, teasingly. " I must say — whoops!" He swung the van as something scuttled across the road in front of them, and the wheels slewed round in the mud, ran across the grass verge and stuck fast. The engine droned pathetically for a few seconds, and then stopped.

" Oh no!" groaned Andy. " wouldn't you just know it!"

" Told you this old banger had just about had it," grumbled Les. There was a clatter as he opened the back doors and jumped down.

Janie's heart sank down into her boots. She knew that this next gig was Spinning Jenny's big chance.

They heard a certain well-known pop promoter was going to be there and though the boys had pretended it wasn't important, she knew perfectly well that it was.

Rich took his arm away, and she missed the warmth. He dropped a light kiss on her forehead, then climbed out to join Les. Andy tried revving the engine again, but it was useless.

Get the instruments out and cover them with the tarpaulin," Andy ordered. " We'll have to push."

Slipping and sliding on the wet surface, they dug their heels in and shoved. The van yielded a little, then stopped and refused to budge. Hopelessly, the group stood back, panting and exhausted.

" We need a tow and some more help," said Andy. " There was a garage back along. What say I walk there and see what gives?"

" I'll come with you," Les offered.

Rich and Janie watched as the two of them went off.

" Let's get back in the front seat," said Rich. " It'll be warmer."

They climbed in, and pretty soon Janie felt her eyelids droop. She leaned her head against Rich's shoulder, and soon felt herself drift off into sleep.

Once she woke suddenly, hearing laughter and scuffling behind the van, but then she saw Rich's eyes were closed and hearing his deep, even breathing was afraid to move in case she woke him.

Some time later, a lorry pulled up beside them, and the garage mechanic soon had the van back on the road.

" Pile everything in," said Andy. " We'll just make it, with luck."

Sleepily, Janie helped with the instruments.

" Here," Les said, as they finished loading. " Where's my guitar?" He began a frantic search. " It's gone!"

They all stood and stared at each other. Janie remembered the noise she'd heard earlier.

" It's been stolen!" Les looked as if he were about to burst into tears. " Someone's stolen it! You sat there and let them take it!"

Andy leaned his head against the door of the van.

" It must've been kids," he said. " It must've been. Some of them saw our name on the side of the van — "

" You're not saying it's been taken for a joke," said Les in a strangled voice. " Well, that's it. That's the finish as far as I'm concerned. Spinning Jenny'll just have to manage without me."

He turned on his heel, and though Andy shouted after him, he refused to look back. Head down, he began striding along the road away from them.

Andy stared accusingly at Janie and Rich.

" I always said girls were no good in a group," he shouted. " They always cause trouble. Now look what you've done. He won't come back. You see. And he's just about the best rhythm guitar we could ever have got. It's all your fault!"

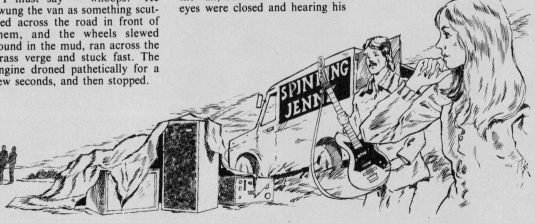

JUST IMAGINE

HERE'S a slightly dotty little quiz for you to try! It's fun to do—and at the end, we'll tell you how we rate your imagination . . . and how you can use it to get most fun out of life!

1—Choose an illustration for " A IS FOR APPLE ", to be used in a child's ABC.

2—What do you think would be most fun to have painted on your bedroom ceiling?
  (a) A colourful design of Chinese rooftops and jolly dragons.
  (b) Kittens playing with balls of wool.
  (c) Clouds.
  (d) Your favourite pop star or other personality.

3—Imagine you can pick the material your school's next summer uniform is to be made of, from the following four designs! Which would you choose?

a   b

c   d

4—Shut your eyes tight and think of the word STAR for a moment. Now tell us what you imagined!
  (a) A single, huge, bright star shape.
  (b) A group of stars twinkling in the night sky.
  (c) A real person who is a " star ".
  (d) Something quite different from any of the above.

5—What do you think this is?
  (a) Melting ice cream.
  (b) Someone hiding under a sheet, about to pretend to be a ghost.
  (c) A blob.
  (d) Treasure Island.

6—You are going on a very long train journey, and can take only one of the following—which would you pick?
  (a) A lively magazine, full of interesting bits and pieces.
  (b) A good long paperback to give hours of reading.
  (c) A notebook and pencil.
  (d) A book of crossword puzzles.

7—You have a very active, sporty friend who has unfortunately just broken her arm. What would you take to cheer her up, when you go to visit her?
  (a) A box of chocolates.
  (b) A book about her favourite sport.
  (c) A set of tiddlywinks.
  (d) Two tickets for you both to go and watch a sporting event she'll enjoy.

8—Meet—well, you choose a name for our little friend!
  (a) Snowball.
  (b) Snowflake.
  (c) Charlie.
  (d) Princess.

9—Which of these girls would you cast for the part of Cinderella in a school pantomime?

a   c

b   d

10—You are asked to " christen " a pudding your mum has invented, which consists of chunks of cold rice pudding, and decorated with blobs of whipped cream, the whole lot sprinkled with chopped nuts. Would you call it.
  (a) Pineapple Surprise.
  (b) Hawaiian Rice Pudding.
  (c) Pineapple and Rice.
  (d) Paradise Island Pudding.

for conclusions see next page

JUST IMAGINE

SCORING

Question 1: (a) 10 points. (b) 7 points. (c) 4 points. (d) 1 point.
Question 2: (a) 10 points. (b) 4 points. (c) 7 points. (d) 1 point.
Question 3: (a) 1 point. (b) 4 points. (c) 10 points. (d) 7 points.
Question 4: (a) 4 points. (b) 7 points. (c) 1 point. (d) 10 points.
Question 5: (a) 7 points. (b) 10 points. (c) 1 point. (d) 4 points.
Question 6: (a) 4 points. (b) 1 point. (c) 7 points. (d) 10 points.
Question 7: (a) 1 point. (b) 4 points. (c) 10 points. (d) 7 points.
Question 8: (a) 4 points. (b) 7 points. (c) 10 points. (d) 1 point.
Question 9: (a) 1 point. (b) 7 points. (c) 4 points. (d) 10 points.
Question 10: (a) 4 points. (b) 7 points. (c) 1 point. (d) 10 points.

CONCLUSIONS

Under 25 points: You are a very straight-forward, open sort of person—but rather unimaginative! You would find it a lot easier to amuse yourself, and find more fun in life, if you started to try to develop that imagination . . . and you HAVE got one, you know!

Try this, some time—cut out any large letters from old newspapers or magazines, trace round them and try doodling inside the shapes they make, filling the blank areas with colour, stripes, flowers or anything you fancy, to make a pattern. Using your imagination is fun, you'll find!

25-50 points: You don't give your imagination much chance—maybe you are a bit timid about admitting that you have one!

Have the courage to try and develop it a little, and you'll find you are a lot more imaginative than you give yourself credit for!

On a boring bus, train or car journey, try inventing a little adventure story about the people or the places you see—imagine how you'd feel if you lived in the tiny village or large town you are passing through. Try to be more observant, it'll give your imagination things to work on!

55-50 points: You have a very good imagination indeed, and could probably be quite creative if you gave yourself half a chance!

If you don't think of yourself as a very artistic or imaginative person, it is probably because you haven't tried the right things, yet!

Have a go at something new—maybe you have a talent for making home-made necklaces, writing stories, inventing, making a garden, decorating cakes, arranging flowers or even modelling with clay or something similar! You can find books in the library that will help to begin, and maybe give you other ideas, too.

If you aren't good at inventing patterns, try folding large sheets of newspaper into four or eight, make random cuts and slashes with scissors, then open the sheet out and use that as a " starter " for your design. With your own imagination to take over from there, you should end up with something very unusual and interesting.

Over 80 points: You have a good imagination, but at the moment you are letting it run away with you rather too much! There IS such a thing as being over-imaginative, you know, and it can lead you into trouble!

Try to keep yours under control—use it creatively (read all the other sections to get some starting-off ideas)—but always have an end result in mind, don't let your imagination wander off too far into the realms of fantasy, and NEVER indulge your imagination to the point where you start inventing things that might just hurt other people!

With a dash of forethought and a pinch of consideration for others, your imagination will help you enjoy your life and find it interesting even when nothing very exciting happens.

THINK THIN!

ROD

Full name: *Roderick David Stewart.* Born: *Highgate, London, on January 10, 1945.* Parents' names: *Robert, Elsie.* Brothers and sisters: *Don, Bob, Mary, Peggy.* Father's occupation: *Newsagent.* Schools: *Highgate Primary, William Grimshaw Secondary.* First ambition: *Professional footballer.* Early musical influences: *Al Jolson, Eddie Cochran, Sam Cooke.* Best school subjects: *Drawing, painting.* Ordinary jobs: *Soccer apprentice, signwriter, fence erector, picture framer, gravedigger.* Groups: *Jimmy Powell and Dimensions, Hoochie Coochie Men, Soul Agents, Steam Packet, Shotgun Express, Jeff Beck group, Faces.* First solo disc: *" Good Morning Little Schoolgirl" (Decca, 1964).* First TV show: *" Beat Room" BBC2 (1964).* First world hit: *" Gasoline Alley" LP (1970).* World record: *Topped singles and LP charts in Britain and America (1971).* Fave performers: *Elton John, Paul McCartney, Gladys Knight.* Personal facts: *Height: 6 ft. Weight: 12 st. 2 lbs. Brown hair and eyes..* Fave food and drink: *Chinese, Mateus rose wine.* Hobbies: *model railways. Soccer.*

Simon

Dave

Tony

Anne

The Discoteers

Ed

Noel

Kid

first loves

"This guy's name was Paul or some thing. But he was a dish. Curly brow hair. The biggest, warmest brow eyes . . ."

THE amber glow of the counter shone steadily but dully as t numbers monotonously climbed downward. An irritati click accompanied each change. Pam's eyes scanned over h bank of check meters. Everything seemed in order.

"Fifteen minutes," crackled ground control.

An air of tension filled the small cabin. Pam looked over at h co-pilot, Sue Denholm, and noticed that her eyes were alme glazed with anxiety. Pam herself was not entirely at ease, but s was sure she wasn't going to waste her yoga relaxations just panic now.

The huge power of the rocket below them was awesome even rest. She tried not to think about it, picked up her command car and began checking off all the little tasks she'd already complete Cabin pressure, check; fuel flow, check; batteries, check; . . . they already been checked about two hundred times, why did they ha to make her go through them again.

"Twelve minutes. All systems check." CHECK, CHECK, CHEC her mind reeled.

The last card was as neatly typed as the others, with the NAS crest boldly emblazoned at the top.

It read, 'To alleviate pre-take off nerves it is advisable converse with other crew members. Preferably about somethi that has nothing to do with the mission.' Below it was scribbled pen, "You girls should be good for this bit, Colin."

Colin Farmer, the Mission Controller, she'd murder him whe they got back. Still, it wasn't a bad idea, but what should she ta about. Sue's eyes were still glazed.

"Feeling all right?" Pam ventured.

Sue spared her a piteous glance.

"Dumb question, huh? Don't worry, these things never fail."

"There's always a first time."

Pam was slightly unnerved by the usually exuberant Sue's to of voice. She sounded really frightened.

"Hey, did I ever tell you how I met Alan?" Pam said jovially

The look on Sue's face betrayed that it was not the subje most close to her heart but she nevertheless shook her head.

"A couple of years ago," Pam said in her most announceri voice, "the TV set belonging to Commander Pamela Firth brol down. Commander Firth of course being the first captain of all-female space crew."

Sue nodded, "Yeah, me."

Pam waved a gloved hand for silence. "Pamela immediate phoned for a repair man. When he arrived, she found him to most attractive."

"Ten minutes, weather good."

"You mean Alan was a TV repairman?" Sue asked.

Pam sighed, "No, this guy's name was Paul or something. B

he was a dish. Curly brown hair, the biggest, warmest brown
eyes . . ."

"I meet them all the time," said Sue glumly.

". . . and he fixed my TV in the twinkling of an eye. He
left after asking me for a date, which I of course refused."

Sue's nod of agreement lacked conviction.

"After he'd gone," Pam continued, "I noticed that my purse
was missing from the mantlepiece where I definitely remembered
putting it."

Sue gasped, "He stole your purse."

"So of course I went right away to the police station to report
it. The guy behind the desk was the handsomest creature you ever
saw alive."

"So this was Alan?" Sue asked.

Pam shook her head, "Patrolman John T. Simpson. He really
fitted that uniform. Those shoulders. So I reported the theft and
went home."

Sue held her hand to her head in despair.

"Seven minutes. And counting . . ."

"Half an hour after I got home a plain clothes man came to
the door. He was quite young to be in plain clothes, y'know. And
he had a moustache."

"This couldn't be Alan?"

"Oh no, this was Detective Sergeant Ferguson. I had to give him
all the details all over again. I told him the name of the TV
company. I described Paul; I even showed him exactly where my
purse had been on the mantlepiece."

"Did he ask you for a date?"

"No, I was going to ask him, but I noticed a wedding ring.
The best ones always get snapped up fast." She made a cursory
inspection of her controls.

"He said it shouldn't take long to capture this Paul fella."

Sue yawned, "How exciting."

Pam ignored her and continued, "I was going to go over to
my mother's and I was driving along this road on my moped when
I saw Paul in his company van turning a corner ahead of me."

This re-aroused Sue's interest, "You're kidding."

Pam crossed her heart, "Nope. Of course I had to give chase,
so I bucked up my trusty steed and tore off after the scoundrel."

"Wow," was Sue's only comment.

"Five minutes . . ."

"Unfortunately I misjudged a corner and bumped into a
Rolls Royce coming the other way," Pam said lamely. "But the guy
driving the Rolls was so nice about it; he was a business tycoon
or something. Just a tinge of grey at the sides and the most
disarming smile . . ."

"Alan?" asked Sue hopefully.

Pam again shook her head, "J. Jackson Tremayne of
Tremayne Industries. He took me to the hospital because I'd hurt
my ankle when I fell off my bike."

"Three minutes, you're looking good for lift off."

Pam hurried on, "The doctor who treated me was a swarthy
Mediterranean type. You know, the kind that adores the way you
walk, is enraptured by the way you talk."

"This couldn't be Alan?"

"Doctor Vishego. He said I'd have to stay in overnight,
plastered my ankle and packed me into a bed."

"One minute and counting, fifty nine, fifty eight . . ."

Pam continued unperturbed, "Two hours later my brother
came to see me in hospital, with a big bunch of flowers. My brother
Billy that is."

"Not Alan," Sue interjected.

"No, not Alan. My brother Billy. He admitted he'd taken my
purse because he was short of money."

"So it wasn't Paul after all?"

"It wasn't Paul," said Pam happily, "Billy had found out what
was going on, had squared everything up with the police and
everybody and he'd brought the flowers as a peace offering.
Wasn't that sweet?"

Sue thought for a moment, "What about Alan?"

Pam slapped her arm rest in mock anger, "Of course, Alan was
Billy's friend. He'd come along to give him some support when he
faced his fearsome sister but ended up falling hopelessly in . . ."

"I don't believe a word of it," said Sue.

"Lift off," said the ground controller.

Starwish

by Muriel-Jane Smith.

EVERYBODY has some idea of what they would like for Christmas. But what about the people who seem to have everything? We went out and about to find out what the stars would like to find in their stockings for Christmas, 1978.

JULIE FORSYTH, the pretty, blonde singer with Guys and Dolls, would like a car for Christmas, so that she can drive herself to singing gigs.

"Ideally I'd like a white Alpha Romeo 2,000. But," she giggles, "I suppose I would settle for a white Mini if I had to."

FAMOUS "friend" of ventriloquist, Roger de Courcey, NOOKIE BEAR, says he would like someone to buy him a fur coat for Christmas.

"I'm getting so fed up with my ' bear ' skin," quips Nookie, "it would be nice to have something to cover myself on chilly days."

RADIO I Disc Jockey, PAUL BURNETT, would be happy to find an Encyclopedia Britannica in his Christmas stocking.

"I've been promising myself for years that I would buy one but have simply never got round to it. Now, perhaps someone will realise I'd really adore to have one for Christmas."

IRISH-BORN singer, DANA, likes to see the people who are talking to her on the telephone so she would like nothing better than a videotape telephone.

"That way I can see everyone who is telephoning me," laughs Dana, " and I would really love that."

"I know that there's the slight disadvantage that I might not always be looking my best when I answer the telephone, but, I think it would be worth it to be able to see the other person as we talk."

SINGING star, LENA ZAVARONI says she's just crazy about clothes.

"But, when I go out to buy them I don't always make the right decisions about what suits me. So, more than anything, I'd like someone to choose a complete outfit for me. And, if they could afford it, it would be nice to have a real leather handbag with matching shoes."

THAT swinging, singing trio, THE THREE DEGREES, would like nothing more than to be given their own personal jet plane.

"You see we travel all over the world regularly every year," explains group member, Sheila Ferguson, " and so much time is wasted at airports, or waiting around. Owning our own plane would cut down all that wasted time."

DISHY actor, RICHARD O'SULLIVAN, longs to be given a reclining armchair in leather, in which he could completely relax, after his long day at the television studios.

"Some friends of mine have such chairs and I've envied them for a long time," says Richard. "When I do get my own chair I'll have a plaque erected above it saying: ' Richard's Chair ', so that everyone will know it is my chair and my chair alone."

THE talented NOLAN SISTERS would like a tennis court, no less, for their combined Christmas present.

"Because we are all absolutely bonkers about tennis," explains the newest and youngest member of the group, thirteen-year-old Colleen.

"Last year, we made friends with the famous international tennis star, John Lloyd, and he really inspired our interest and now we all play tennis. We could just about fit a tennis court in our back garden at Ilford."

ESSEX APPEAL

ESSEX APPEAL

JANIE

PART THREE

JANIE was never more glad to see anyone than she was to see Les waiting for them, all smiles, at the hall.

It had been a terrible journey, with neither Rich nor Andy saying a word.

They'd trooped into the dressing-room, and there he was, complete with guitar. Apparently it had all happened just as Andy had said it would.

A fan who had had a ticket for the concert had thought it would be a giggle. It was fortunate that Les's temper had cooled down and he'd decided to hitch a lift and re-join the group.

"Magnus Perrivale is here," Andy reported, after a surreptitious look through the drawn curtains. "Talking to someone at the back of the hall. They look familiar, but can't quite place them."

"Talent scouts," said Rich gloomily. "They make all sorts of promises but nothing ever comes off."

"Maybe this will," said Janie. "I've got a sort of feeling in my bones."

"Rheumatism," chuckled Les.

But Janie really did feel that after all their troubles the evening was going to go well.

She'd bought a new outfit with her, a deep frilled black and red gipsy skirt with a black velvet scoop-necked top. She planned to wear a red bandeau over her brown hair and some shiny gold hoop earrings.

During the time the boys had spent at her house, she'd helped Rich compose a new song: "Farewell Gipsy Lady." Tonight would be the first time they'd performed it in public. It just had to be a success.

"You look great, Janie," said Rich, when she was dressed and ready. "Much better than Pearl ever was."

Janie felt a glow of happiness sweep over her. Although to be the singer with a famous group had always been her ambition, she wasn't quite so single-minded about it as she had been.

Now the dream included Rich . . . and not only as the drummer of Spinning Jenny. He meant much more to her than that.

She followed the boys out onto the stage. Rich began to discuss their lighting with the stage manager.

To begin with, and during their opening number, the stage would be in almost total darkness. Then for " Farewell Gipsy Lady " the red spotlight would pick out Janie, and the boys in their garb of gaily-coloured Romany outfits would be covered in blue. It was a dramatic number, with a very good strong beat.

Janie was fine until the glow of the spot suddenly shone on her, and Rich began a soft insistent drumming in the background.

She felt her legs start to tremble, and for one awful moment she thought she might faint.

She missed the opening bar, faltered and then came in on the second. Out of the corner of her eye she saw Andy, saw him staring at her, felt him almost willing her to get it right.

It meant so very much to all of them.

And then suddenly she lost her stage fright, and it began to come together, the song, the group, the audience.

Janie really became the poor forsaken gipsy, left by her faithless lover and destined to spend the rest of her life alone and forgotten.

As the guitars died plaintively away and Rich's soft drumbeat brought the song to its final end, there was silence in the hall. Then, a tremendous tumult of clapping and people surged to the edge of the stage, shouting. It was some time before they could carry on with the rest of the act.

Afterwards, there were scores of fans queueing up for their autographs. Janie, hot and tired, had never felt happier in her life.

After a while, the crowd melted away and the four of them sat on the floor of the dressing-room completely exhausted.

" We've made it," Andy said triumphantly. " We've finally and completely made it. It was that song that did it. You and Janie, Rich, you'll have to write all Spinning Jenny's material in future. S'only a matter of time before Magnus Perrivale signs us up. After tonight he must give us a recording contract."

Rich pressed Janie's hand, his eyes sparkling.

Then the door swung open, and the little man they had seen talking to Magnus Perrivale came in.

" That was great," he said enthusiastically. " Great. Only wish old Magnus had been able to stay and see it. Unfortunately he was called away before you came on stage."

Janie and the boys stared at the little man, hardly able to believe their ears. They'd set such store on the big record producer.

And he hadn't even heard them . . .

FOR LOVE OF LENI...

IN the year 2278 a very superior kind of person had grown up alongside normal humans.

These people, the Astras as they were called, had the power to read minds. Because of this and the gleaming star shape on their foreheads, the Astras were disliked and mistrusted.

Shayla and Andra were two such girls . . .

They continue to think we pry into all their little secrets, Andra.

And that's why they hate us . . . it is a great pity.

Look! The one in the red tunic, Andra. He is so handsome.

Mmm, pity he's not one of us . . .

The good-looking guy was called Leni.

Right, boys, we'd better get going if we want to make it to the carnival.

The Mayor's Charity Carnival. I'd forgotten. D'you fancy going?

Why not. We'll maybe get a chance to see that boy again.

Later, at the girls' apartment—

I'm going to cover my star . . . first time I've ever risked doing it.

What? Why?

We won't get anywhere near the boys if they see our stars and I want to see how the other half lives.

So, at the carnival.

This is more like it. Look, the mayor's about to make a speech.

My son, Leni, and I would like to thank . . .

At bedtime.

He's bound to find out you're an Astra, y'know.

No, he won't—I'll take care. He really is dreamy and I'm seeing him tomorrow again.

Next day at the swimming pool—

Come on—last one in is an Astra!

As Shayla surfaced, Leni gasped in dismay—the water had faded Shayla's make-up on her star.

Shayla . . . you're a . . . a . . . an Astra!

As Leni strode off.

Leni . . . Leni . . . wait . . . I can explain.

Back at the apartment.

I told you this would happen, Shayla. You took a chance.

I know, I know, but I think I'm falling in love with Leni.

64

But Shayla began to read the memory of the girl and soon saw the faces of the kidnappers.

So, later at the police station.

Rogues' gallery, miss. Yes, follow me, but why you want to see it, I don't know.

At the video screen.

It's him. That's the man who kidnapped Leni.

What is that man's address? I must see him.

So—

Bradigan? 'E' moved, miss. Try Calico Drive.

At number Ten Calico Drive.

Bradigan? Never heard of him.

He's lying. I can see into his thoughts. Leni's tied up in there.

Some girl snooping about, Brad.

Forget it. The ransom money's as good as ours.

67

Shayla picked up the revolver.

You stay put—or YOU'LL get the gun.

Later, when Shayla had freed Leni and contacted the space police.

What can I say? But why did you do it? I walked out on you.

You followed my thoughts of course. That must have led you to where the kidnappers were holding me.

No, you're wrong, Leni. One thing an Astra can't do is read the mind of somebody we love! All you get is a kind of fog. A love fog.

SWEET SCENTSATIONS

IT'S said that a girl who doesn't wear perfume is as disappointing as a beautiful flower which has no scent!

Fragrance is something a boy never fails to appreciate; but the kind guaranteed to switch one fella on can turn another right off!

It all depends on his Zodiac sign, and certainly not on how much you paid for that bottled magic!

Every sign has a ruling planet, and just as there are planetary colours (for example, red for Aries), there are planetary perfumes.

ARIES
MARCH 21—APRIL 20

ARIES is a Fire sign, ruled by Mars. The planetary fragrance is definitely sharp and spicy; the kind to make your boyfriend's senses sizzle.
Some suggestions:

His senses are very keen and he gets a real lift from the scents of Eastern goodies like cloves, vanilla, pimento, ginger, ginsing and patchouli. The soft fragrance of woodsmoke which forms the perfume of picnic fires pleases him too, though.

Bronnley's 'Lime' fragrance is spicy and refreshing, in a whole range of bathtime goodies.

Crabtree and Evelyn's 'East Indian Lemon and Spices' and 'West Indian Sicilian Limes' are extra special, exciting colognes. The bottles are special too; exact reproductions of 19th century ones.

Miners 'Eastern Ginger' perfume stick; the easiest lightest way to tote perfume in your cosmetic bag or jeans pocket.

TAURUS
APRIL 21—MAY 20

TAURUS is an Earth sign, ruled by Venus, whose planetary perfume is sweet and warm. Avoid sharp scents, and choose romantic ones containing the rose which is the flower of Venus, and with musky, dusky depth to give them strength and staying power.

Some suggestions:

Even if you're not wearing perfume, keep that Taurus boy seeing you through rose-coloured spectacles, by making your bath soap one which leaves a lingering, rosy fragrance.

Crabtree and Evelyn's ' Tudor Rose ' is in a choice of rich ' Damask ', ' Musk ' which has hints of honey and pollen, or wild, apple-scented ' Eglantine '.

Yardley's ' Red Roses ' with matching talc makes the right impression on his nose too!

Coty's ' Smitty ' is fruity, flowery and musky with ingredients ranging from tangerine to mousse de chene, and including roses. The effect is quite light; but very lasting!

Rimmel's ' Rosie ' is a sugar and spice perfume with a rose right in its romantic heart.

Yardley's ' Je Suis ' contains Palma roses and the lily like ylang-ylang, a flower whose scent is very potent.

GEMINI
MAY 21—JUNE 20

GEMINI is an Air sign, ruled by lively Mercury whose planetary perfume is crisp and fresh. The guy born when the Sun was in Gemini hates sultry scents, but does like smart, subtle, rather sophisticated blends; the ' bright lights ' perfumes.

Some suggestions:

' Lemon Verbena ' meaning ' you enchant me ' is good as a light, everyday fragrance, and many famous perfumiers including Culpeper, Bronnley and Floris have a full range of verbena scented bath time basics (everything from bath oil and soap to hand lotion).

As a special occasion perfume Dior's exhilerating ' Miss Dior ' is sure to be appreciated by the Gemini nose.'

Replica's ' Dewth ' is crisp and smells much more expensive than it is.

Rimmel's ' Cancan ' is smooth and sweet for disco dates.

CANCER
JUNE 21—JULY 21

CANCER is a Water sign, ruled by the Moon. The planetary perfume is delicate and romantic. The Cancer boy dislikes scent which socks itself to him, so keep it light.

Some suggestions:

Boots ' Blue Fern ' spray mist, backed up by bath time goodies in the same feather light fragrance, including bath foam and talc, or Goya ' Aqua Citra ' range.

Goya ' Gardenia ' which, strangely enough contains jasmine.

Yardley ' Flair! ' The gardenia, jasmine and tangy bergamot it contains add up to the perfect Cancer combination.

LEO
JULY 22—AUGUST 21

LEO is a Fire sign, ruled by the Sun, and the planetary perfume is warm and sweet. The Leo boy likes a power-packed potion, but remember any scent containing musk intensifies on the skin, so go easy on it.

Some suggestions:

Goya's ' Aqua Manda ' range, especially their oatmeal complexion soap and gorgeous golden foam bath, for a basic scent as warm as mellow sunshine.

Max Factor's ' Rapport ' smells very French and sophisticated, with exciting undertones of patchouli, sandalwood and musk strengthening the floral and citrus notes.

Rimmel's ' Ego ' parfum de toilette is another rather unusual one containing scented woods, spices and musks.

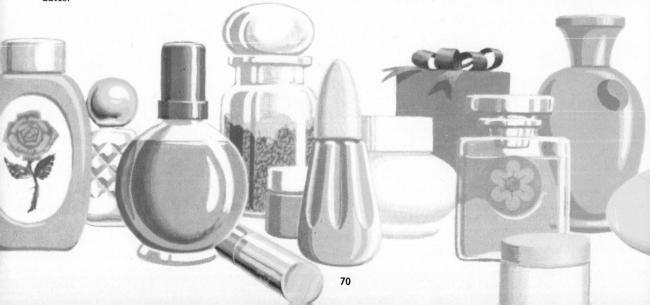

VIRGO

AUGUST 22—SEPTEMBER 21

VIRGO is an Earth sign, and, like Gemini, ruled by Mercury. The Virgo boy likes clean, crisp scents, with a herbal base and dewy 'garden-in-the-rain' freshness—they keep him wide awake to your charms.

Some suggestions:

For bath time basics, New Day 'Herbal Tonique' foam bath is refreshing, and a real bargain. Use a soap like Bronnley's 'Rosemary' and while your skin is damp, splash with Boots No 7 New Formula 'Rosemary and Cider Vinegar' before towelling dry.

Coty 'Muguet de Bois' is the classic pure perfume of lily of the valley and has that green note Virgo boys appreciate.

Jackson's of Piccadilly 'Old Manor House Cologne' is a real pot-pourri perfume.

LIBRA

SEPTEMBER 22—OCTOBER 22

LIBRA is an Air sign, and like Taurus has romantic Venus as a ruling planet. The Libra boy favours rich, bouquet perfumes which are sweet and warm. Bypass the tomboy blends and choose classic ones which have a fragrant air of elegance.

Some suggestions:

Boots 'Original Formula' 'Rose Flower Perfume' and 'Lavender Flower Perfume' in globe-shaped smoked glass bottles with tiny corks look and smell good and make ideal, everyday scents partnered with two soaps super for skins. 'Original Formula' 'Oatmeal and Lavender' and the 'Rose and Almond Oil'.

Coty 'L'Aimant' meaning 'the magnet,' is a classic perfume sure to please the Libra boy. It contains orange blossom and roses, both flowers of Venus, amongst many other goodies.

Floris 'Red Roses' is the real thing!

Rimmel's 'Butterfly Rose' fragrance stick for a light whisper of scent to make you the lass with the delicate air.

SCORPIO

OCTOBER 23—NOVEMBER 21

SCORPIO is a Water sign, ruled by Pluto, planet of the mysterious underworld of mines and caves! The planetary perfume should have hidden depths; like that Scorpio boy himself.

Some suggestions:

Bronnley's 'Thume' or Culpeper's 'Wild Thyme' soap, and Just Herbal foam bath for a herby bath time brew-up.

Coty 'Styx', spell spinning spray mist or 'Witches Potion' creamy skin perfume (there's also a 'Quicksilver' talc).

French Almond 'Ginsing' perfume spray. The chief ingredient is an exotic Eastern herb, said to have magical power!

Lentheric 'Tweed' honey sweet yet peaty.

Yardley 'Chique' is warm with roses, jasmine, patchouli (a magical Eastern plant) and Sandalwood.

SAGITTARIUS

NOVEMBER 22—DECEMBER 20

SAGITTARIUS is a Fire sign, ruled by Jupiter. The planetary perfume is sweet and mellow, but the cheerful Sagittarian hates heavy scent which punches

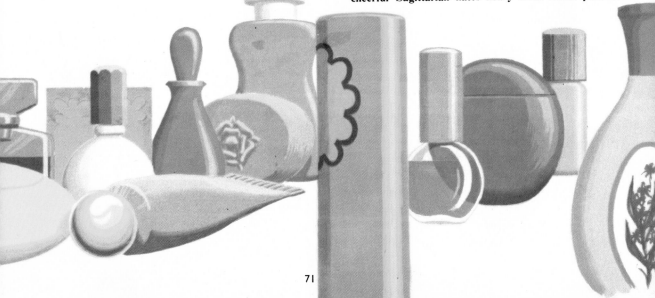

him on the nose! He loves the warm, smokey, mossy kind.

Some suggestions:

Boots 'Almond Blossom' bath goodies range (including spray mist) to give a light yet warm fragrance for everyday.

Faberge 'Woodhue' mellow and resiny.

Goya 'Shuni' holds hints of leather and incense as well as warm amber, woodsy and floral notes. The name is that of a Red Indian goddess and the cologne spray comes with a talisman necklet, the perfume in a tiny bottle adorned with a leather thong and beads. There is a matching talc and turquoise-coloured bath foam.

Yardley 'Laughter' fresh and green on the surface with a warm heart of spices, scented woods, flowers and patchouli.

CAPRICORN
DECEMBER 21—JANUARY 19

CAPRICORN is an Earth sign, ruled by Saturn, and the planetary perfume one of evergreens and scented woods. The Capricorn boy likes classic scents, and appreciates those which are fresh and yet have an underlying richness.

Some suggestions:

Bronnley 'Sandalwood' bath range including soap-sponge which is super for showering, and splash cologne. Boots have a Sandalwood range too.

Coty 'Masumi' is melon-like and mossy, and contains unusual goodies like mimosa and violet leaves.

Tiki 'Honey Water' made to the same recipe used in the days of the Roman Empire thousands of years ago contains nutmegs and elderflowers as well as orange, clove and rose.

AQUARIUS
JANUARY 20—FEBRUARY 18

AQUARIUS is an Air sign, ruled by Uranus, planet of new awakenings and change. The planetary perfume is one of wild flowers and springtime. Choose a fragrance light as a summer breeze and avoid exotic, sophisticated blends.

Some suggestions:

Bronnley 'Wild Flowers' range of soaps, bath oils, bubble baths, colognes and hand lotion, are just right for the girl who wants to appeal to an Aquarian.

'Wild Blue Anenome' is a springtime fragrance as fresh as the original lilies of the field.

'Wild Mignonette' used to grow wild in London. The Empress Josephine made it fashionable and as 'reseda' its French name, the essence is used in many expensive perfumes.

'Wild Pink' is the gillyflower brought to England by William the Conqueror. Its scent can still win admiring attention. Violets are other flowers which give a fresh impression. Amongst super ranges are Floris 'English Violet' Grosvenor 'Devon Violets' and Yardley 'April Violets'.

Yardley 'Sea Jade' is a sharpish, sophisticated blend of violet and sandalwood.

PISCES
FEBRUARY 19—MARCH 20

PISCES is a Water sign ruled by Neptune. The perfume associated with this planet is sweet, subtle and seductive, so choose a really romantic one. The Pisces boy doesn't like scent to come on too strong though, so keep your fragrance haunting and elusive!

Some suggestions:

Tiki 'Norwegian Kelp' soap and 'Sea-Weed' bath extract in the 'wild herb' range, or Boots 'Seaweed Bath Essence' for starters. Crabtree and Evelyn 'Cormoran Ylang-Ylang' exotic cologne. A captivating scent.

Floris 'Ormonde' a bouquet scent like a well stocked country garden.

Yardley 'Shanida!' This has all it takes to make a perfume sweet and subtle, with the added tang of citrus and excitement of spice.

Last but by no means least, if the perfume which makes you feel good has no effect on him except to make him wrinkle his nose, or the kind he likes makes you feel quite sick and headachey—he is not really your kind of guy. Your nose knows, you know!

ON a warm summer's day in 1942, when Mary Harrison and her family arrived at a small seaside inn, they little knew what strange adventures lay in front of them . . .

The Raven

Mary's father had been wounded in the war with Germany, and had chosen the seaside to convalesce.

Mm! Smell that fresh air! What a difference from London!

Look! It's called The Raven. What a quaint name!

Fetch, boy!

Later, Mary and her brother Terry took their dog Kirrie for a walk.

I do hope Dad will feel better after this holiday, Terry. He looks so drawn.

Suddenly—

Come back, Kirrie!

It's a bird, Terry, and it looks hurt!

There, there! We'll soon have you fixed up.

That's a raven you have there, Mary.

But, when they arrived back at the inn . . .

Get that bird out of here! Out, I say!

But why?

The landlord was adamant, so there was only one thing for it . . .

The vet will take care of you, little bird!

He's got a bad break in his wing, but given time—

Wonder what the landlord of the Raven meant when he said, 'When the raven returns, ill-luck follows its footsteps.'

Later, unseen, Mary managed to smuggle the bird into her room . . .

There now, I'll keep you safe. I don't believe any of that superstitious nonsense!

A few days later . . .

I'm off in a boat with Dad and Terry today, so keep quiet. I'll see you tonight.

However, before the trio had covered any distance . . .

Dad! Dad! Are you all right!

Of course, I'm all right. Stop fussing!

But—

Dad!

Making their father as comfortable as possible, they set off for home.

Just take it easy, Dad. Soon be home.

Meanwhile, back at the inn—

Kirrie! What is it? What's the matter, boy?

Kirrie! Come back!

Oh, Kirrie, you've let Mary's raven escape!

Kirrie, please stop!

Back at sea the small boat had drifted hopelessly off course in the night . . .

Terry, do we have to go much further? Dad looks terrible.

Just then—

It's my raven! He can fly!

Mary! The oar! You've dropped the oar!

Oh, I'm sorry!

So you should be! Seems the landlord was right about that stupid bird!

Now it's deserting us! It's a bird of ill-omen, right enough!

But wait! It's not going in the direction of the shore—

As if hypnotised, the family followed the raven's course, until—

Look! There's a little island!

There are no sharp rocks here. We'll make it!

We'll have to camp here overnight, I'm afraid.

Poor Mum! She'll be worried stiff about us!

Early next morning, they left the island with a makeshift oar—

Eventually, they reached shore safely.

Richard! Children! Oh, you're safe! I was so worried!

I can't believe you're safe.

It was the raven who led us to the island, Mum. He made sure we were safe till daylight.

The raven! But that's impossible! Look!

The Raven Inn was a blackened shell.

The inn was hit by a bomb last night.

It happened just after Kirrie and I chased outside after the raven, but I'm sorry—

The raven was struck by a car, Mary. He died instantly.

But if he hadn't led you and Kirrie outside, Mum, you'd have been in the inn when it was bombed—

—and they called him a bird of ill-omen! I'll never forget you, wherever or whatever you are. You saved all our lives!

79

CHARLIE'S MAGNIFICENT SEVEN

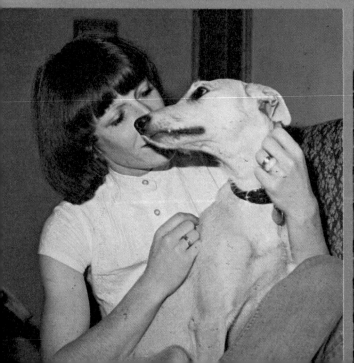

CHARLOTTE CORNWELL, known to her mates as 'Charlie', and better known to TV viewers as Anna, one of the "Rock Follies" Little Ladies, has the most amazing collection of pets.

Most of us have, perhaps, a dog or a rabbit, well Charlotte has several of these, plus — would you believe — a snake!! Or to be exact, a five-foot Boa Constrictor!!

Her entire pet collection — seven in all — consists of a mongrel, two lurcher dogs, two rabbits, a horse and, of course, the snake!

"I've always been very keen on animals," she explains, "so my 'family' just kind of grew. Alice is a very lovable dog.

"One day I was wandering around Battersea Dogs' Home when suddenly I saw this pleading little face staring at me, and that was it, I had to take her home. That was about four years ago.

"She's a very sensitive dog who will always come and sit by me whenever I'm upset, whereas the two lurchers will just carry on tearing up and down the stairs.

"However, on one occasion Alice did cause me a bit of embarrassment.

"Whenever Michael, my husband, and I go anywhere we take the dogs with us. So, when we went to the first Nedworth Open-Air Pop Concert, the dogs came too.

"We were lucky enough to get passes to admit us to the Press enclosure, which enabled us to sit right at the front of the stage.

"During the show Van Morrison walked onto the stage to perform, and right in the middle of his first number — Alice decided she'd join in!! She held her head back, opened her mouth and howled!!

"I was blushing with embarrassment while everyone around shook with laughter — everyone except Van Morrison!! I don't know why, but I don't think he appreciated Alice's performance too much!!

"The other two dogs are both lurchers.

"The original lurcher was a greyhound crossed with a collie, which gave it speed, intelligence and the ability to poach.

"Flute, the mother, is a deerhound-greyhound cross, third generation and she had her first litter at the end of last year.

"Gypsies, who originally bred lurchers, say that you should always keep the first born with the black face. We did.

"Now, as you can see, her black face has gone completely and she's left with just black rings around her eyes, a very black nose and the rest of her is the colour of champagne. She's called Rabbit.

"If you put the lurchers outside with some rabbits or squirrels they'll go for them, but in the house they're as soft as butter. You may think it strange having two rabbits in the house!

"When we just had Flute she knew that she couldn't touch them, but as soon as the puppy came they tended to encourage one another so now I have to keep an eye on them.

"I was walking past a stretch of grass in Fulham, not far from our house, when suddenly I saw a bunch of kids swinging this poor creature around by its ears. I was absolutely livid but they ran off and dropped the poor thing on the grass.

"He was petrified, so I carefully carried him home and he's been with us ever since.

"The snake, named Guiseppe Fatoc-cini, used to belong to my nephew but when he went to Oxford University he was given to me, because for some reason or other, students aren't allowed to keep Boa Constrictors in their rooms!!

"Michael is an interior designer and he keeps Guiseppe in his study, inside a huge tank which he made for him.

"It's like an aquarium without water and we've put in gravel, logs, plants and things to make him feel at home.

"Every year Michael goes off to the Isle of Man for the T.T. racing and last year while he was gone a friend stayed with me. She went into the study to say 'Goodnight' to Guiseppe when suddenly she yelled out, 'Charlie! The snake's gone'! I thought she was kidding, but she wasn't!

Snakes need a lot of heat so I'd put an extra-hot light bulb inside his tank. It had melted the side of the wood, the bulb had blown, and once it had cooled down he'd managed to slide past it and through the hole.

"We searched for days, but he didn't materialise, so we assumed that he'd left us for good.

"Then one day I was talking on the phone when suddenly I saw him. He crawled out of a cupboard and up the side of the bookcase, near to where we hadn't finished flooring.

"I put the receiver down, grabbed him and put him back in his box. He was completely black with the cold, because he has to be kept in a temperature of about 85 degrees and obviously it was pretty cold and damp under the floorboards.

"Finally, my horse, Nance, is in Wales. I use her for breeding and she has a foal a year.

"If one year she produces either a pure chestnut filly or a pure bay filly then I'll keep the foal as well. Other than that I think I've got enough animals for now — until we decide to buy a bigger house and open our own mini zoo!!"

ARE YOU A SUPER SISTER?

IF you were a fly on the wall, would you hear nothing but praise from your brothers and sisters? Or could there be a harsh criticism or two? Your answers to our quick Quiz will show how you rate in the sister stakes.

You are baby-sitting with the youngsters while your parents are at the firm's Christmas dinner-dance. There's a ring at the door and your best friend says, " Come and join us. There's a super party on." You:—
a) Refuse firmly and give the reason.
b) Say, " Let me check first that they're asleep."
c) Ask the youngsters if they are okay. If they seem happy, leave them.

Your cute little brother (or sister) gets all your parents' attention. You:—
a) Are too busy with school and friends to let it upset you.
b) Realise he (she) needs more attention than you do at this stage and try not to let it get you down.
c) Feel horribly jealous and are (tell the truth) beastly to him/her.

You persuade your sister to lend you her new blouse for Saturday's party. You:—
a) Return it looking perfect.
b) Forget it isn't yours for keeps.
c) Return it in need of washing.

Your kid sister is always delving into your cosmetics. Gets you down and no wonder! So you:—
a) Give her lip shine, cream, nail polish and eye shadow for birthdays and Christmas.
b) Keep your treasures under lock and key.
c) Tell her off good and proper!

Your sister brings home a dishy boy friend you sense immediately is attracted to you. You:—
a) Find an excuse to go out.
b) Do your best to get him to ask you out.
c) Treat him like any other boy you know.

Because you're the sister who's good at managing money you're always being asked by the others for ' a loan '. You:—
a) Lend, giving a time limit for return.
b) Lend, though pretty sure you'll never see it again.
c) Refuse outright.

Your brother has that super pal you fancy. You:—
a) Dress naturally, make your appearances short and sweet, play it cool.
b) Follow the two fellows like a shadow, to big brother's annoyance.
c) Dress up to the nines when HE's around.

Because you're bright, you're always being asked to help with homework. You:—
a) Coach the kids in their weaker subjects so that they can tackle their own homework.
b) Take over completely and do their homework when asked.
c) Say you're too busy, 'cos you can't spare a minute away from your boyfriend.

You know your sister is still friendly with a girl/boy with a bad reputation whom your parents consider bad company. You:—
a) Have a talk with your sister and ask if she's SURE she's doing the right thing.
b) Tell your parents.
c) Do and say nothing.

Your overweight brother or sister is trying desperately to lose weight. You:—
a) Help by eating sensibly youself in front of him/her.
b) Delight in nibbling sweets and crisps in front of them.
c) Laugh and imitate when you see them doing slimming exercises.

Your parents can afford to send either you OR your sister on that school trip to Paris. You:—
a) Suggest it should be your sister, though really you'd love to go.
b) Suggest it goes by seniority, the older sister going this year and the younger of the two next year.
c) Insist it should be you because you're dying to see Paris.

Your brother or sister has been waiting for half an hour to use the 'phone but your friend hasn't finished speaking to you yet. You:—
a) Say to your friend, " I'll have to go in two minutes. The 'phone is needed."
b) Ignore your brother or sister.
c) Deliberately prolong the conversation to show who's boss.

Now to tot up your score:—

MOSTLY A'S

YOU'RE a sis in a hundred, and if they don't appreciate you they should. Funny thing is, though, that you're so well-balanced, so easy to get on with, that they may not even realise what a super sister you are!

Take care you don't get ' sat upon ' by any of the brothers or sisters with a bossy nature.

MOSTLY B'S

YOU'RE a sister of character, an individualist with, let's face it, a tendency to tease and a strong desire to get your own way! Never reluctant to make a decision, you can be exceedingly mature and wise, or the reverse.

To become more popular with the others, control that selfish streak in an otherwise likeable nature.

MOSTLY C'S

YOUR attitude to your brothers and sisters tends to be negative. If anyone is in trouble , you are seldom the one to whom they turn. Yet this is partly because you yourself are well able to stand on your own two feet and expect the same of others.

More consideration for the younger ones will make you better liked. A kinder attitude all round is needed.

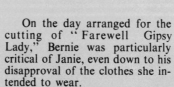

JANIE

PART FOUR

IT seemed funny to Janie when she thought about that night and the way Magnus Perrivale had missed their act.

It was only a few short weeks ago, but it seemed like a lifetime. They'd all been so miserable and gloomy that they hadn't taken in a single word of what the little man said.

Finally, he'd almost had to shout at them to make them understand.

It appeared he was a friend of Magnus's, a talent scout who was on the lookout for any promising new groups.

And apparently he was very impressed with Spinning Jenny and their new song. So much in fact that he wanted them to call at the recording studio and cut a demo disc.

It had all seemed too wonderful to be true. Janie and the boys had discussed their future over and over together.

" You'll need a manager now — a proper one," the little man — whose name was Flint — told them. " I think I know just the chappie."

From the very first time she met him, Janie had somehow disliked Bernie Caulder. She couldn't have said why, and she tried to stifle the feeling. But it was there, all the same.

She kept quiet about it, however, because the boys were so enthusiastic.

" Knows his stuff, does Bernie," Andy kept saying. " Not much about the pop world he doesn't know."

Perhaps that's why he keeps finding fault with me, Janie thought miserably. He seems to be driving me and the rest of the group apart.

On the day arranged for the cutting of " Farewell Gipsy Lady," Bernie was particularly critical of Janie, even down to his disapproval of the clothes she intended to wear.

" It's got nothing to do with him," she told Rich tearfully. " I mean, we're not on television or anything."

" Well," said Rich awkwardly, patting her arm and looking worried, " I should just go along with him, love. I mean he's the boss really, isn't he? He knows how to sell the group. We need him."

" We managed all right before," Janie said rebelliously. " He doesn't like me, Rich."

" Rubbish." For a second Rich looked impatient. " You're imagining things, Janie."

But she knew she wasn't.

She put all thoughts of Bernie aside however when they went into the big, soundproof studio. She stifled her nerves, determined to make a really good job of the recording. It was so important to all of them.

Bernie and Mr Flint sat in a little sort of control tower way up near the roof, earphones clapped to their heads. Janie tried to pretend they weren't there.

Bernie however made sure that she knew.

Over and over between " takes " he found fault with her phrasing, her diction, her presentation. This was wrong, that was wrong, she wasn't trying hard enough. Bit by bit he was destroying Janie's confidence. Even the boys were worried, particularly Rich.

" Don't let him grind you down," he whispered to Janie. She could sense the puzzlement in his voice.

And then, quite suddenly, she saw a slight movement in the pool of shadow at the back of the recording studios.

She saw Bernie half-turn and give the thumbs' up sign to the figure of the girl standing there.

Janie had never seen her before, but she'd seen a picture taken with Spinning Jenny when she'd been the singer of the group.

It was Pearl.

And she and Bernie Caulder were obviously hatching some plot up between them. A plot to get rid of Janie and replace her with Pearl.

In those few seconds, everything became clear to Janie. Pearl wanted to rejoin Spinning Jenny now that they were on the road to making a name for themselves.

Determination put new strength into Janie, and she sang as she'd never sang before.

The record was in the bag.

Bernie got up without a word.

But Andy wasn't going to let him get away with it so fast.

" Bernie!" he called. " Bernie! I want a word with you! And Pearl. That was her over there, wasn't it? I'd like to see her too."

So Andy had seen what had happened. The important thing was, what was he going to do, and how would it affect Janie? Trembling, she waited as Bernie turned and strolled towards them.

CINDER NELLIE

Anyone who thinks glass slippers went out with Cinderella—is absolutely right!

But if you can live with a hob-nailed boot—read on.

Mmm, I'd love to go to the disco tonight, but my two sisters reckon I'm too young. All I'm good for is ironing their gear! Oh, I'm Penelope by the way—Nellie for short!

Hey, haven't you finished yet, Nellie?

Stop day-dreaming and press-on with our outfits. (Press-on, —get it, Oh, never mind.)

Mmm. If only I had a new jump suit or velvet jacket I'd show them . . .

From apple to one oily motor bike in a flash.

ZAP

Tch. I AM getting careless. Must be hungry or something. Still, it's better than nothing.

This is a nightmare—not a dream. But I'd better humour the fat, old pest—er, sorry, the dear old thing!

Well, disco—here I come. For better or for worse.

VAROOM

Poor, fat Nellie in her hob-nailed boots was the laughing stock of the disco. But one guy wasn't laughing.

CRUNCH

Hmm! It's an ill wind. Things are looking up for Nellie.

DISCO

The disco really rocked as Nellie and her tubby partner tripped—sorry—murdered—the light fantastic!

Hey, you're all right, Nellie.

Then—

Hoi! Cherub! Come back—I wanted to run you *home* on my tandem.

AARGH! Midnight. Time I made myself scarce! We're still trying to follow the Cinderella routine, y'know!

All that was left for poor Arnold Hepplethwaite III was one very heavy hob-nailed boot!

DONG DONG DONG DONG DONG

As midnight chimed poor Nellie's faithful bike began to fade.

THUMP!

And—WALLOP—she was left driving a two-stroke Granny Smith—

SPLAT!!

OOYAH! What a shambles of a night that's been. Still, I'm back to my old self again.

—which, to add insult to a bruised bottom, bounced up and hit her in the head.

88

HAVE YOURSELF A CAPITAL TIME

WHO knows, you could find yourself on holiday in one of our great capitals this year. If you do, we have planned an exciting programme for you, to make sure you enjoy every single precious minute.

LONDON

MONDAY

TOWER OF LONDON (Tower Hill, E.C.3. Tower Hill. Tel. 01-709-0765). See the Crown Jewels . . . Tower Ravens . . . armour for horses and elephants! There's covered seating for a picnic if it's wet, or picnic by the Thames. Also HMS Belfast, Royal Navy cruiser with 7 decks to visit. (θ Tower Hill then ferry from Tower Pier. Tel. 01-407-6436). If you want to see one-man submarines and Colditz souvenirs, the Imperial War Museum (θ Lambeth N. Tel. 01-735-8922).

TUESDAY

Hampton Court Palace. (Tel. 01-977-8441. BR. from Waterloo. Or by boat from Westminster Pier, passing Kew and Richmond—super on a good day). See the Great Vine and try not to get lost in the Maze! Picnic in grounds or by the river. Eat at the Tilt Yard Restaurant, or cafeteria. See the State apartments of this splendid Henry VIII royal palace, the Tudor tennis court and kitchens.

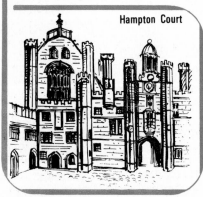

Hampton Court

WEDNESDAY

Madame Tussaud's, Baker St., (θ Baker Street, Tel. 01-935-6861). See wax figures of pop singers, sportsmen, Sleeping Beauty who actually breathes! Also Planetarium nearby (Tel. 01-486-1121) where the Zeiss Star Projector transports you through space and time. Then on to Regent's Park, where there's sailing and rowing on the lake from March to October. And/or the London Zoo, Regent's Park, an animal-lover's paradise.

THURSDAY

St. Paul's Cathedral, Ludgate Hill, E.C.4. (θ St. Paul's. 01-248-4619) Built by Sir Christopher Wren 1675-1710, see for yourself the magnificence of the second largest Christian church in the world. (Best to visit on a Sunday if you wish to attend a service.) Also Museum of London, London Wall, 01-600-3699 to see models and rooms from every period including 18th century prison cells and the Great Fire of London with lighting and sound effects. Benches outside are ideal for a picnic lunch. Also Monument (Monument θ) 202' high reached by 311 steps. Wonderful view from top and wonderful way of keeping in shape because—there's no lift!

FRIDAY

National Gallery, Trafalgar Square, WC2. θ Trafalgar Square/Embankment.) Here you will see some of the most famous paintings in the world. Say 'hello to Nelson on his Column in Trafalgar Square as you leave. You might like to walk along the Strand, browsing in the shops. Take a look at the famous Savoy Hotel, then into the Embankment Gardens for cafe or picnic lunch, where there could be a band playing. Also board HMS Discovery, Victoria Embankment, (Tel. 01-836-5138) the ship in which Captain Scott explored the Antartic. Also if time and inclination, whip up to Marble Arch for a visit to Selfridge's and the West End stores.

SATURDAY

Houses of Parliament, St. Margaret St., SW1. θ Westminster (01-212-4781. Closed Saturday before State Opening of Parliament). See House of Commons, House of Lords, Strangers' Galleries. Also Westminster Abbey with its tombs of the Kings and Queens of England, Poets' Corner, Coronation Chair and Stone of Scone. Look out for the Churchill Statue in Parliament Square, erected 1965. Complete the day with a London theatre, ballet and opera or a concert at the Festival Hall.

Houses of Parliament

SUNDAY

Speakers' Corner, Marble Arch. (θ Marble Arch) to hear all the world airing an opinion on a Sunday morning. Or Petticoat Lane's famous market (things to wear, things to eat) Aldgate East θ or Liverpool St. Stn. Followed by an afternoon on Hampstead Heath (Hampstead/Golders Green θ then bus 210. Visit lovely Kenwood (tea and ices available) or wander along Hampstead's quaint Heath Street. (If it happens to be a Bank Holiday you'll be lucky enough to see Happy Hampstead's two colourful fairs).

EDINBURGH

MONDAY

STROLL along world-famous Princes Street. Lots of souvenir shopping possible if you've the time—and cash! Visit the Scott Monument (Sir Walter, who else!) at East Princes Street Gardens. Climb the 287 steps to the tower top (whooh!) for wonderful views of the city. Lunch in the Gardens. Explore The Castle overlooking Princes Street, steeped in history: see the Royal Apartments, Great Banqueting Hall and Scottish Crown. Along the Royal Mile to St. Giles Cathedral, stopping at Lady Stair's House (built 1622) to see original writings of Robert Burns, Sir Walter Scott and R.L. Stevenson.

St Giles'

TUESDAY

At St John's Church, West End, try your hand at brass rubbing, a fascinating hobby. At Royal Scottish Museum, Chambers Street, enjoy outstanding sections on space flight, natural science, plus interesting films. In the Royal Mile, see toys from down the centuries at Museum of Childhood. And at The Wax Museum, 142 High Street, see a lifelike Mary Queen of Scots and Bonnie Prince Charlie, and visit the spooky Chamber of Horrors—if you dare!

(For more details about what to see, contact London Tourist Board, 26 Grosvenor Gardens, London SW1W 0DU, Telephone 01-730-3450).

θ=Underground

WEDNESDAY

Complete contrast today! Bus or coach takes you 10 miles to Hopetoun House at South Queensferry, a superb Adam Mansion with parkland, deer, majestic peacocks and rare St. Kilda sheep, black with four horns! Enjoy a rooftop tour of the House, and see the unusual exhibition 'Horse and Man in Lowland Scotland'. At Biggar south of Edinburgh, a fascinating reconstruction of 19th century village shops is well worth a visit.

Hopetoun House

THURSDAY

Visit Hillend Ski Centre, Pentland Hills, the largest artificial ski slope in Britain. Wonderful walking country. Ride the chairlift to the top and gaze down on five counties. Open all year round, the Centre is floodlit on winter evenings. Great! If swimming's your choice, try the Commonwealth Pool in the city, or Portobello's Open Air Pool with wave-making device, and room for 3000!

FRIDAY

For a day at Edinburgh Zoo, take a 12, 26 or 31 bus from Princes St. See the world-famous penguin colony; the Carnegie Aquarium; the special miniature farmyard. Enjoy a pony ride. Great shots to be had if you're a photographer. There may be some tennis to see at Craiglockhart, or a football match at Easter Road or Tynecastle. See the local papers for concerts, plays and films for entertainment.

SATURDAY

Visit Meadowbank Sports Centre, London Road, a super sports complex with facilities for about 30 different sports. Temporary membership available for visitors. Sightseeing again, see The Palace of Holyroodhouse (Buses 1,45,60) the Queen's official residence in Scotland, where Mary Queen of Scots lived for six years and Rizzio was murdered. Impressive State apartments and portraits of over 100 Scottish Kings. Stamp collectors will enjoy the Philatelic Bureau displays in the Post Office, Waterloo Place. Or visit Scottish Craft Centre, Royal Mile (Buses 1,45,60) for a display of Scottish crafts.

Holyrood House

SUNDAY

See Kirk of the Greyfriars, Greyfriars Place on the site of a 15th century Franciscan Friary. Services most Sundays. Go to nearby Candlemaker Row to see the statuette of Greyfriars Bobby, the Skye terrier who after his master's death in 1858 watched over his grave for 14 years. For one of the biggest collections of rhododendrons in the world, visit The Royal Botanic Gardens, Inverleith Row. A blaze of colour!

Bird lovers might prefer a visit to the beaches near Dunbar, North Berwick and Kirleton—a favourite for ornithologists.

For further information contact Scottish Tourist Board, 23 Ravelston Terrace, Edinburgh, Phone 031-332-2433.

CARDIFF

MONDAY

CARDIFF CASTLE, in the heart of this seaport capital, occupies the site of a Roman stronghold. Magnificently rebuilt last century, it asks to be explored both outside and in. Look out for the richly ornamented Clock Tower 165 feet high, the Guest Tower and guest rooms including Bachelors' Bedroom, Arab Room and Chaucer Room with stained glass windows illustrating the Canterbury Tales. Now for some contrast, walk through lovely Bute Park and join the throngs of Cardiff teenagers having a lunch-time sandwich. Next, to the main shopping streets, St. Mary St., Duke St., Queen St., and The Hayes where you'll find everything from the trendiest fashions to Welsh pop records—if you've the lolly!

TUESDAY

Visit the Welsh Folk Museum, St. Fagan's, (Tel. 561357) and you'll be in a bygone age. Actual cottages, chapels, workshops, farms and mills have been placed in the parkland setting of St. Fagan's Castle. Look out for the Costumes Gallery if you're interested in what a girl would wear hundres of years ago. Super picnic area. Now to the tiny Cathedral city of Llandaff (via Cathedral Road) with its tranquil, old-world air. Cathedral is famed for Epstein's 'Christ in Majesty'. Make for Chapter Workshops and Arts Centre, Market Road (Tel. 25776) where you'll see potters, painters, antique restorers and puppet makers at work. Could inspire you to copy! Tea available!

Welsh Folk Museum

WEDNESDAY

Fancy some sea today? Bus to Penarth, South Glamorgan.

Choice of sailing, water skiing, fishing, beach fun. Culture lovers will enjoy Penarth's Turner House Art Gallery late morning or afternoon. In Plymouth Road (Tel. 708870), contains Turner prints, fine porcelain, oil paintings by Rosetti and other famous paintings. Look out for Tom Rathwell's "The Sideboard"—untidiest ever!

THURSDAY

A visit to Castell Coch, just 5 miles NW of Cardiff, will give a day worth remembering. This fairy-tale castle peeping through trees high on a hill above the Cardiff-Merthyr Road is like something out of Hans Andersen! The castle is approached only by a wooden drawbridge over a dry moat. Look at the 'Lord's' and 'Lady's' bedrooms with their painted beds; ceilings gleaming with golden stars; murals depicting Aesop's Fables. Descend to the gloomy dungeon if you dare! Back in Cardiff, how about a swim at the Empire Swimming Pool (near Bus Station).

Castell Coch

FRIDAY

The National Museum of Wales, Cathays Park (Tel. 26241) proudly awaits your visit in the capital's civic centre. Make your way to the Glanely Gallery where forest, lakeland, mountains and seashore are realistically depicted. See the re-creation of the interior of a coalmine. Makes you feel you're there! Amongst the paintings look out for Renoir's famous 'La Parisienne'. Afternoon, if you'd

like to visit local Crafts and Rural Industries look at the local papers. Pottery, Welsh dolls, lovespoons, Welsh tapestry including fashionwear are usually on show.

National Museum of Wales.

SATURDAY

If you're under 16 and like dancing, join the Saturday morning dancing session at Top Rank Cardiff Suite, Queen Street. If you prefer squash, badminton, swimming, fencing or some other sport, make for the Sports Pavilion in Sophia Gardens. Handy for a picnic lunch on the banks of River Taff. Should pitch-and-putt be your mood, visit Llandaff Fields, Heath Park or Trelai Park. Fairwater Park has a ski slope and for a spot of riding try the Equestrian Centre at Pontcanna. In the evening, if you're in luck, the Welsh National Opera Company could be at the New Theatre. Good film choice always at the Queen Street cinemas. Check the evening papers.

SUNDAY

Visit St. John's Church, with its beautiful steeple, in bustling St. John's Square. Just one hour's drive from Cardiff is the Brecon Beacons National Park, super for hill walking and a paradise for nature lovers. If you've artistic leanings, try sketching the grand sweep of these grassy mountains! Alternatively, if you fancy swimming, boat trips, or yachting, make for the resorts of Penarth, Barry Island, Porthcawl or Abervon, easily reached by public transport if needed.

DUBLIN

MONDAY

LET'S start by visiting Dublin Castle, high in the city centre. From here take in City Hall, Christ Church Cathedral and St. Patrick's Cathedral. Fresh air wanted? Take a bus to Botanic Gardens, Glasnevin. Founded in 1795, this 'little Kew' of 50 acres is filled with rare plants and shrubs. See where Parnell and O'Connell lie buried in Glasnevin Cemetery.

Dublin Castle

TUESDAY

Visit the famous Phoenix Park, Europe's largest city park, which covers 1,760 acres! (Comfortable shoes advised!) Look out for the President's home (Aras an Uachtarain), Papal Nunciature, Phoenix Park Racecourse, and of course, the Zoo. Dublin Zoo is specially noted for breeding lions. You may be lucky enough to spy some playful cubs, and see the pelicans and flamingos on the two natural lakes. Ample picnic space. If you want to watch some hurling (like hockey but more spectacular) Croke Park is the place to go. Enquire at Tourism.

WEDNESDAY

A day for some exercise maybe. Tennis at public courts, Herbert Park, Ellenfield Park or Johnstown Park (only 3p an hour if you're under

For additional information contact Wales Tourist Board, Welcome House, High St., Llandaff, Cardiff CF5 2YZ. Tel. 0222/567701.

18). Or Pitch and Putt (details from Tourism) or golf at Howth Public Golf Course (9 miles from city centre) or beach fun at nearby Dollymount, Sandymout and Merrion. If bikes are needed, contact Raleigh Rent-a-bike, 8 Hanover Quay, Dublin, 2.

THURSDAY

For souvenir shopping take a walk along the famous Grafton Street which leads to the imposing O'Connell Street. Even window shopping is fun! If music is your scene, Switzers, and the Kilkenny shop are the places for Irish discs. For a spot of culture, make for Chester Beatty Library, 20 Shrewsbury Road. See the priceless treasures left to the Irish nation by the American mining millionaire when he died in 1968—rare Chinese books inlaid with jade and gold, and the oldest known New Testament manuscript. You're near to the Civic Museum, 58 South William Street, to delve into Dublin's adventure-filled past.

St Patrick's Cathedral

FRIDAY

Let's enjoy Dublin city itself again. See the magnificent Custom House where, at the Registrar-General's office you can try to trace your own Irish ancestry if you have any. The National Art Gallery and Municipal Gallery of Modern Art are musts for the art-lover. For an open-air lunch amongst the city's students and young office workers, make for

St. Stephen's Green. You're in the right area for Trinity College, University College, Government Buildings and a general tour of inspection.

Custom House

SATURDAY

Bullock Castle, Dalkey. Reached by no. 8 bus. (Tel. 806993 to find out when open). See this restored 12th century 'fairy' castle overlooking picturesque Bullock Harbour. Filled with treasures, and a Victorian Nursery. Explore the pleasant town. The rock-enclosed pools are great for bathing. Visit nearby White Rock Strand and Killiney beach backed by cliffs and hills. Evening: the famous Abbey Theatre for real Irish drama. Or ballad and music concerts (see evening papers).

SUNDAY

To start your day, there's a great choice of church services. Plane spotters can nip on a No. 41A bus for Dublin Airport to view one of western Europe's best-equipped airports from a fine observation platform. Country lovers can make for Lucan and Leixlip, pretty inland villages on a wooded stretch of the Liffey. Or for a day by the sea, there's a lovely sandy beach just ten miles away at Malahide. See evening papers for film and other entertainment news.

For latest tourist news, contact Dublin Tourism, 51 Dawson St., Dublin 2. Tel. 747733.

Sound Yourself Out

IT can be one of your most valuable and attractive assets all through life, both at your job and socially. Are you sure it does you justice?

With the help of a leading speech instructor to famous names of stage and TV screen, we can help you have the right voice for the right occasion.

FIRST, what do you sound like? There are two ways to tell, says our expert. For Method One you need a medium or high-priced tape recorder. " A cheap one won't do," we're told. Excellent results are obtained if these rules are followed.

Use the tape-recorder in a room where there are curtains, cushions, carpet and not too many windows. The average sitting room would be ideal. Don't make the recording where there are unrelieved, high walls.

The second way to know how you sound is simple and cheap. Put cotton wool in both your ears and press it in. Now speak, and you will hear your voice as it sounds to others. Speak for a full two minutes to get the complete effect, and if you don't know a poem by heart, a paragraph or two from today's paper, or Mum's shopping list will do.

How did you sound? In the Angela Rippon class or not quite?

Not many of us have her near-perfect diction, a hint of humour and music in the tone, the full meaning brought out in every word.

Perhaps you found your voice surprisingly shrill or low, twangy, indistinct, words swallowed, hesitant or gabbling—in fact, thoroughly disappointing. If so, let's get together with our speech expert and benefit from those speech secrets.

YOUR VOICE AND WHAT YOU CAN DO ABOUT IT.

High voice, usually too loud. The sort we've all heard giving the plot away two rows behind at the cinema, or disturbing concentration while we try to select a book at the library!
Cause:- Tension in the larynx (voice box), or in the neck, or both.
Treatment:- a) Try to speak the first words of your sentences in as low a pitch as you can manage without growling. This sets a lower tone.

b) Do this relaxing exercise regularly. Breathe in, drop your head back slightly and speak with one hand pressed against the end of your breast bone. Press the breath out while you are speaking.

You should feel your voice come from right down at the bottom of your lungs, not from your larynx and neck.
Quiet, indistinct voice. You've probably been told "Speak up!" more than once.
Cause:- this is usually lazy articulation.

Treatment: a) To make mouth loose and mobile instead of half closed, stand in front of a mirror and move your jaw up and down, ten times.

Next, to make tongue agile and firm, with jaw open, press tip of tongue against upper teeth ridge, then against lower teeth ridge. Begin slowly, gradually increasing in speed.

b) With mouth open, poke your tongue out and stretch it up in an effort to touch your nose. Then put your tongue out and down. Repeat several times. This strengthens your tongue and improves clarity.

Gabbling speech, words swallowed. It's a strain on the listener to make out what's being said.

Cause:- either a highly-strung temperament, or too anxious to get everything out at one go, or even too small a vocabulary!

Treatment:- practise reading aloud, making sense of each little group of words. Before you read, divide every sentence into groups of words, laying stress on the words with most meaning. It must make sense.

Nasal, twangy voice.

Cause:- the jaw is held stiffly, so that the tongue can't move freely, the mouth being half shut. Result: vowels thin, consonants sloppy.

Treatment: let your lower jaw drop open and try to breathe in through your nose. When you've finished breathing in, breathe out through your mouth.

Next, with your mouth open, breathe in through your mouth and when you've finished breathing in, with your mouth still open, breathe out through your nose.

Do this for five minutes. If possible do it at odd minutes during the day, specially just before you are going to speak. This exercises your soft palate muscles.

Harsh voice. Gives the impression, often mistakenly, of being unfriendly.

Cause:- muscles of neck, shoulders and jaw held stiffly. This gives the effect of swallowing. Larynx (vocal box) is tightened, vocal chords strained and the sound produced is harsh and discordant.

Flat, monotonous voice. Can be particularly 'off-putting' on the phone this type of voice, and has made many a fellow think twice about asking a girl out!

Cause:- a droner sounds dull and bored because the same value is given to every alternate word.

Treatment:- this reflects way of thinking and is not a voice problem as such, so should be comparatively easy to cope with.

Join in with anything tuneful on the radio, to exercise the tonal range of your voice. Remember that a bored voice is boring to listen to.

Use cheerful, interesting voices, as examples to copy.

And finally, a quickie exercise for anyone who wants a pleasant voice and clearer consonants.

With teeth apart and jaw open, practise saying "Cool", "Calm", "Crowd", "He". But don't do it in front of the mirror or you won't be able to stop laughing.

Treatment:- a) Several times a day, specially if you're feeling tense, flop and go limp. Others won't notice, but you'll feel all the better.

b) Twice a day spend five minutes on any arm-swinging, shoulder rolling exercises you've learnt in P.E. classes.

c) Copy a voice improvement trick practised by many TV and stage personalities before an important appearance: yawn, stretch and relax.

MENACE by MOONLIGHT

Jill Gordon and Katie Forbes were on a climbing week-end in the Scottish Highlands.
As they enjoyed a cup of hot tomato soup on the summit of Ben Mhor . . .

Well, we made it—but the weather's turning. I don't like the look of these clouds.

Time we finished this grub and headed back.

But a sudden blizzard caught up with the girls before they had gone very far.

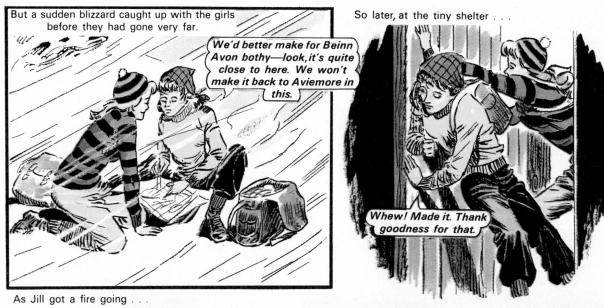

We'd better make for Beinn Avon bothy—look, it's quite close to here. We won't make it back to Aviemore in this.

So later, at the tiny shelter . . .

Whew! Made it. Thank goodness for that.

As Jill got a fire going . . .

Someone's left a fair bit of wood—it'll be cold tonight.

Listen to this. Last entry in the log tells that John Cairns should have been back here by mid-day today. Must have been him that gathered the wood.

His gear's still here—clothes, food . . . he can't be far away.

But later—

Look! Snow's stopped. It's getting dark, but we'll have to make an effort to get back to Aviemore. This man Cairns could be out there with a broken leg—or worse—it's well past mid-day!

The girls put on their warmest clothing . . .

This tea will keep us warm for a bit. Good job we know how to read the compass. We'll need it in the dark. Right, let's go!

But the cottage door wouldn't budge—

Hey! The door's locked. We can't get out! Who could have done that?

But why?

Standing on a chair, Katie tried the skylight window.

Good! We can get out this way.

PING! A shot rang out from the darkness and ricocheted from the metal chimney.

What the . . . ?

It's crazy! But someone's taking pot-shots at us out there!

Then we'll have to find another way out!

So, in a small back room the girls began to prise some loose planks from the wall.

We've made it. But keep low. Shots came from the other side. We'll be hidden from view from whoever's watching us. Make for those trees.

Right! So far so good. Let's get moving. I've a strange feeling we're in danger.

As the girls moved off, a silent figure on skis armed with a rifle glided after them.

The sinister pursuer dogged the girls' every footstep.

As the moon glistened on the snow-covered hills . . .

Come on, Jill. The moon will show us the way to Aviemore.

CRACK! A rifle shot shattered the night air—

Look out! AVALANCHE! That shot started it!

The avalanche swept down on Jill and Katie. But using the correct "swimming" motion they rode it.

Till finally they came to a halt.

Are you all right?

Just a bit shaken.

Two KIDS! Girls!

A gruff voice behind them made the girls start.

Should have taken a warning, girls. No questions please! Get moving!

Later in Sinclair bothy, a shelter similar to the one which Jill and Katie had not long left, were two men. One, bound to a chair, was John Cairns.

Cairns explained . . .

I was trying to stop a top spy known as Borisoff, from getting out of the country. He's the one in the brown anorak.

We weren't much help.

Not your fault, girls. They're professionals, this lot. My bet is they are waiting up here for their contact.

Next morning.

Chopper coming now.

But the helicopter wasn't the one Borisoff had been expecting!

They're ahead of schedule!

What the—who called for the R.A.F. Mountain Rescue service?

Jill and Katie sprang into action.

But it was the two spies who were 'grabbed'

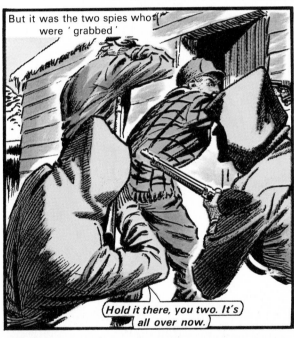

Word was sent to intercept Borisoff's approaching helicopter.

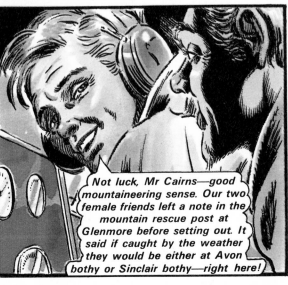

That night, Jill and Katie relaxed with the R.A.F. boys.

KEEP YOUR COOL WITH Cologne

FROM THE TOP:

Hair lacks bounce and shine, and you haven't time to shampoo it? Make several partings in your tresses, soak a piece of cotton wool in cologne and dab it along them to make your scalp feel fresh.

IN days gone by, a bottle of Eau de Cologne stood on the dressing table of every fashion beauty. She didn't use it as a perfume, but as a beauty aid, to keep her looking and feeling good from top to toe.

Bottles of cologne that are big in size and low in price can be super Christmas presents for girls who have younger brothers and sisters; or mates with keen eyes for bargains!

Here are a dozen ways you can use that wonderful stuff to be at your best and most well-groomed for a date.

Comb cologne through your hair and put in some rollers, if you're having a bath; but if only your fringe looks lank, dampen it with cologne, put in a roller and dry it right away with a hairdryer.

AFTER YOUR BATH:

Splash on that cologne, while your skin is still damp, then towel yourself briskly to give your circulation a real buzz. Classic Eau de Cologne, provides the perfect background scent which adds a fresh note to your fave perfume.

WHISPER SWEET NOTHINGS:

A few drops of cologne—just two or three—added to a full glass of water makes a fragrant mouthwash which gives your mouth a cool, clean feeling and ensures your breath is as sweet as your talk.

ON THE SPOT:

If you see a spot starting to rear its ugly head, a dab of Eau de Cologne could nip that in the bud.

SMILE SWEETLY:

Who hasn't found the toothpaste tube squeezed dry when she was rushing to be in time for a date?

But a teaspoonful of bicarbonate of soda mixed with a tablespoonful of cologne makes a super substitute which is good for gums as well as for brushing teeth.

HANDS UP:

Take a tip from Victorian girls and put a dash of Eau de Cologne on the palms of your hands. Rub it in to give that rosy look, like the inside of a shell, which makes a pretty hand even nicer to hold in the back seat of the cinema.

FRESH TO YOUR FINGERTIPS:

Dip a cotton wool bud in cologne and smooth it over your nails after removing polish. This helps strengthen them.

FEELING HEADACHEY?

When you get uptight, dab some cologne on that heated brow. Then sprinkle some on your palms, cup them over your face and inhale, to clear your head. This is a Victorian tip for curing the vapours!

KEEP IT LIGHT:

If the gorgeous perfume your boy friend bought you seems a bit too much of a good thing, tone it down by putting just a dab of the concentrated scent on a little piece of cotton wool soaked in ordinary Eau de Cologne.

Tuck it into your brassiere, or smooth it over your pulse points. These are inside wrists and elbows, behind knees, on the temples and where your hairline starts on your brow and the back of your neck.

AND SO TO YOUR TOES:

Splash tired tootsies with Eau de Cologne and you'll be able to keep on dancing—all night!

And there you are, fresh as paint and looking as if you'd just stepped out of a bandbox, thanks to your bottle of cologne. To complete your good grooming don't forget the final touches.

SET MAKE UP:

Pour a few drops of cologne on a tissue and dab it over your face. This is a god way of having a quick freshen up too.

HOT TIP

In sticky summer weather, keep your hair cologne bottle ice cold in the fridge. This makes it doubly refreshing.

JANIE

PART FIVE

OF course, everything had turned out all right. The boys had been so incensed at Bernie's duplicity and his obvious close friendship with Pearl that they'd refused to work with him.

Finally, Magnus Perrivale had taken over, and since then Spinning Jenny had never looked back.

"If only "Farewell Gipsy Lady" would shoot up the charts," sighed Rich. He was sitting in the foyer of the hotel they'd booked in at the previous night, with Janie close beside him.

Magnus had fixed for them to open a new boutique, emphasing that the publicity would do them a lot of good. Afterwards, they would sign copies of their new discs to every fan who purchased one.

"All part of the plan," said Andy with a grin. "After all, the Beatles and the Rollers had to start like this. Anyway, what say we take a look round the town while we've got the chance? Won't be much time in the morning."

It was the first time Janie had been in the Midlands, and she set out holding Rick's arm, eager not to miss a single thing.

The last place they visited was a dimly-lit disco, which they'd nearly passed by without noticing. It was in a side-street, approached by a steep flight of steps which led down to the basement. Rich went first, with Janie close behind him.

In the darkness of the room with the soft sigh of a slow rhythm number all round them, she melted into the warmth of his arms. She felt she could have stayed there forever.

Then the music changed to a fast, pulse-throbbing reggae number.

Janie wasn't sure, afterwards, exactly when the trouble started. One minute she'd been smiling at Rich, trying to talk to him over all the strident noise and the next, bodies seemed to be flying everywhere.

She saw Andy bending down, trying to help up a long-haired lad in a denim suit who'd been pushed by another, bigger boy who was crashing and slamming about in all directions.

Then a girl spun across the floor and cannoned into Janie.

For a minute everything went dark, until she felt Rich's arm about her and his whispered "Come on, let's get out of here."

He elbowed his way towards the door, closely followed by Les and Andy.

There, a number of people seemed to be pitching in on one solitary boy in the middle of them.

Without a thought, the Spinning Jenny boys waded in to rescue him.

Janie stood back, her heart swelling with pride.

Then, she heard the screech of whistles.

It was all over in a matter of seconds, before anyone knew what was happening.

She was bundled with the others into a police van, nobody paying the slightest attention to her protests. She couldn't even see Rich, or Les, or Andy.

But she saw them all right when the van reached the police station. She also saw the reporters, notepads at the ready, eyes gleaming at the prospect of a story.

If only they don't discover who we are, she thought desperately. The publicity'll kill us stone dead. We weren't involved but no one'll ever believe us. She saw the boys looking at her and knew they were feeling the same way.

If only they'd stayed in the hotel, if only they hadn't gone to the disco!

One by one their names were taken and recorded.

At last it was Spinning Jenny's turn. Janie stepped forward first. She saw one of the girl journalist's eyes suddenly widen, and her heart sank.

She saw her whisper to one of her companions, and then they both came hurrying across.

"Well, well!" said the first one. "Who'd have thought it! You're the new rave group, aren't you — Spinning Jenny? Expected to take the music business by storm. You've done that all right, haven't you?" Her companion began to slip her camera from her shoulder.

"Should make a great story, even if it's not exactly the one you wanted. No — " she held up a hand as Janie tried to speak — "don't say a word. I'll get my facts from some of the others here, if you don't mind. An unbiased report. That's what my paper likes to be absolutely unbiased."

With a wave of her hand she moved away. The group stood together, silent, united in their misery.

Was this to be the end of the road for Spinning Jenny?

The Fair Maid of Fouroaks

IN the midsummer of 1651, Charles II was living the life of a fugitive after an unsuccessful effort to wrest his kingdom back from the power of Oliver Cromwell and his Roundheads—

Your Majesty, we must find somewhere of greater safety than this. The place is alive with Cromwell's troops.

✳ ✳ ✳ ✳

Charles and his companion, Lord Wilmot, fled to Fouroaks, the home of Colonel Lane, a trusted royalist. Living with the Colonel was his lovely seventeen-year-old daughter, Jane.

✳ ✳ ✳ ✳

Make sure we have sufficient food, Jane, we expect guests for dinner.

'Tis not often people come visiting in these troubled times.

When the guests arrived—

These are our guests, Jane, dear.

Oh! I expected gentlemen. Shouldn't they dine in the kitchen, Father?

So, you would put your King to eat with the servants, would you?

The King! Oh your Majesty, forgive me.

There is nothing to forgive, Madam. I doubt even my own mother would recognise me at this moment!

Later—

Much as it grieves me I can see no other course but to flee once again to France until more favourable times arrive.

The countryside is seething with Cromwell's troops, your Majesty. It will not be easy reaching a port.

I have a plan, if his Majesty would do me the honour of listening.

Daughter, this is no matter for women. Kindly be silent.

Nay! Mistress Jane. Please, share your plan with us. We have not such a surfeit of them that we can turn any away unheard.

I have a pass for myself and a male servant, Will Jackson, to travel to Bristol. If your Majesty would not mind playing the part of a servant, you could go in Will's stead.

A servant is better any day than a hunted fugitive, my pretty one!

At Bristol, sire, mayhaps you would be able to hire a craft to take you to France.

It is indeed a worthy plan, but the risks are high. Don't forget, there is a thousand pounds on my head. You would be in grave danger.

My daughter is fully aware of the risks involved, but we are proud to be loyal Royalists. She has my blessing to go ahead.

Thank you, Father.

I thank God that I still have some loyal subjects. I only hope that one day I can fully repay the help you have given me.

Early next morning, the party left Fouroaks—

I shall ride ahead and scout for danger, Sire. You may be reassured I shall never be far from hand should you need my services.

Thank you, Wilmot.

My Lord Wilmot is a good man but I would feel much happier had he agreed to wear a disguise.

Your own is perfect, Sire. You look an ideal servant.

Then you must treat me as one, Mistress Lane. It is not usual to address one's servant as Sire!

Of course not, how stupid of me.

Goodbye, dearest daughter. Godspeed on your journey.

Fear not, Sir, no harm shall come to her while I have breath left in my body.

The day passed uneventfully. At nightfall—

Aye, I can let you have a room for the night, Madam. Your servant can find himself a corner somewhere.

But—

Some of these men were at the Battle of Worcester. I fear they may recognise me.

But we cannot leave now, that really would arouse their suspicions.

110

Over supper—

You provide excellent fare, Landlord, but I am more grateful for the shelter. One does not feel safe with that rogue Charles Stuart at large.

Indeed not, Madam. But there are notices everywhere bearing his description. Let us pray he may be speedily brought to justice.

It might be brought about more swiftly if the notices gave more detail than that of "A tall, black man upwards of two yards high". Why! That description could be applied to my servant, Will Jackson, here, and it would indeed be a lucky day if anyone would give me a thousand pounds for him!

I saw Charles Stuart at Worcester and he was at least three fingers taller than your man, Madam.

Later—

Well we have come safely through one day, but the road to Bristol is still long, and there is danger in every step.

Next morning, they had barely started their journey, when—

Sire, there is a battallion of Cromwell's troops ahead, scouring the countryside for you.

It will take more than your clever tongue and quick wits to save me this time I fear, Jane. These men will not be as dim as were those at the Inn.

But the King reckoned without Jane—

Sire, quickly into the hedgerow. I have a plan, but Wilmot must make himself scarce.

Swiftly, the pair changed clothes—

There! Only remember that you are a poor, dumb soul and we may yet evade capture.

Minutes after they resumed their journey—

They would appear to be in order. But why do you not speak, Madam? Is an officer of Cromwell's too lowly a being for your favour.

Alas, Sir! My lady has been struck dumb from birth. A great sadness to her father.

Just then, Wilmot created a diversion—

Methinks we should enquire why that man is in such a hurry. Quickly, after him . . .

Oh, dear! Lord Wilmot has drawn their attention from us. But if they should catch him...

Have no fears on that account. Wilmot is too good a horseman to be caught by that rabble.

Before too long, they reached Bristol, without any more mishaps—

The time has come when we must part, but rest assured that you will always have a special place in my heart and thoughts my dear, brave Jane.

I pray it will not be long before Charles regains his rightful place on the throne. It has been a great honour to have helped, even in such a small measure, to bring that end about.

I Remember, I Remember

PAUL NICHOLAS

" . . . my father picked me up by my ankles, holding me upside down and then lifted me up and down as though he was one of those men flattening tar on the road!

I was under the impression that all kids played this game with their dads and I just couldn't work out why I was the only kid in my class with a flat head!! "

SUZI QUATRO

" . . . being very jealous of my little sister Patti when my mother brought her home for the first time. She was such a beautiful baby, so I bit her fingers.

I was only three at the time, but I've never forgotten it, and then several years later, when I was about twelve I was crying in bed. When she asked me what was wrong I told her that I was sorry for what I'd done nine years earlier!"

DEREK PASCOE
(FLINTLOCK)

" . . . sitting in my high chair. I must have only been eighteen months old, and spilling a cup of tea all over the floor!

This must have been about the time that things started sinking in, because I can remember that same week being given a boiled sweet which I swallowed and got stuck in my throat! "

CHARLOTTE CORNWELL
(ROCK FOLLIES)

" . . . lying inside my pram and somebody putting the flap up at the front because it was starting to rain.

I always used to hate it when they did this because it made everything seem so black and eerie, and however much I screamed it made no difference. Ever since then I've been petrified of the dark."

Turn a few pages for more pop memories

DAVE BARTRAM

Birthday: March 23.
Instruments played: Guitar, keyboards, harmonica.
Fave singers: Ray Charles, Gladys Knight.
Musical education: Piano lessons.
Fave colour: Royal blue.
Car: Porsche.
Fave food: Indian.
Hobbies: Songwriting, football, country life.
Fave actor/actress: Charles Bronson, Julie Ege.
Ambition: To combine success with happiness.

BUDDY GASK

Birthday: December 18.
Most thrilling experience: Learning to fly.
Fave singers: John Denver, Melanie.
Previous occupation: Own musical instruments firm.
Fave single/album: "House Of The Rising Sun"/"Buddy Holly Collection."
Family pet: Boxer called Buster.
Fave actor/actress: Paul Newman, Bette Davis.
Hobbies: Flying, boating.
Ambition: To have own recording studio.
TV debut: "New Faces."

AL JAMES

Birthday: January 13.
Previous occupation: Blacksmith.
Fave singers: Paul Rodgers, Tina Turner.
Biggest influence: Paul McCartney.
Education: Church Langton School.
Likes: Sunshine, snow.
Dislikes: Bad manners, cakes.
Car: Rolls Royce Corniche.
Fave single/album: "Summertime Blues," "Band On The Run."

ROD DEAS

Birthday: February 13.
Previous occupation: Clerk.
Fave singers: John Lennon, Millie Jackson.
Car: Ferrari B.B.
Fave actor/actress: Burt Reynolds, Lassie.
Likes: Sunshine.
Dislikes: People who talk too much.
Most thrilling experience: Driving a racing boat.
Instruments played: Guitar, bass.
Pets: Two dogs and a horse.

THE SHOWADDYWADDY SHOW

ROMEO CHALLENGER

Birthday: May 19.
Fave colours: Brown, black.
Biggest influence: Beatles.
Fave clothes: Snake-skin, leathers.
Car: Can't drive, take taxis!
Fave food: Curry.
Hobbies: Chess, football.
Musical education: Drum lessons for sight reading.
Most thrilling experience: Playing at Isle of Wight Festival.
Fave composer: Stevie Wonder.

TREVOR OAKES

Birthday: September 9.
Instruments played: Guitar, harmonica.
Fave clothes: Jeans, T-shirts.
Car: Jaguar.
Fave food and drink: Lemon meringue pie, milk.
Biggest influence: Pete Townsend.
Face actor/actress: Steve McQueen, Bette Davis.
Hobbies: Football, football and football!
Fave singers: Paul Rodgers, Bette Midler.
Musical education: Self-taught.

RUSS FIELD

Birthday: September 1.
Fave colour: Dark blue.
Education: Loughborough University.
Fave singers: Paul Rodgers, Nina Simone.
Pet: A cat called Oz.
Fave actor/actress: Donald Sutherland, Jane Fonda.
Hobbies: Reading, collecting musical instruments.
Biggest influence: Hank Marvin.
Most thrilling experience: Driving racing car.
Likes: Punctuality, animals.
Dislikes: Blood sports, formal dinners.

MALCOLM (THE DUKE) ALLURED

Birthday: August 27.
Education: Mundella Boys' School, Leicester.
Fave colours: Black, dark blue.
Hobbies: Horse riding, spinning discs.
Biggest influence: Elvis.
Fave clothes: Jeans, suits.
Fave food: Indian.
Instruments played: Drums.
Fave singers: Elton John, Maria Muldaur.
Fave actor/actress: Charles Bronson, Susan George.

A DREAM COMES TRUE

"DIANA" readers often write to us, asking if we'll help to make a very special wish come true. When thirteen year-old Susan Huxtable, from Stoneleigh, Surrey, wrote us asking if we could fix it for her to meet her favourite pop star—Alvin Stardust, Alvin was only too happy to oblige and here is the story of Susan's dream come true.

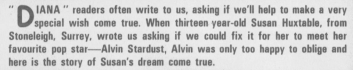

A DAY on the canal was Susan's choice of meeting place and, where better than Little Venice, a London beauty spot, where the romantic canal is dotted with boats of every description.

Susan, her long, blonde hair, brushed until it shone, was wearing a pair of brand-new jeans, which she'd persuaded her mother to buy her for the occasion. And, it was a case of "snap," when Alvin greeted her at the door, also wearing jeans.

"Now I can wear mine and not feel out of place,"

she told me. "I felt really shy at the thought of meeting Alvin but, after we'd shaken hands and he'd driven me in his car to Little Venice, I felt I'd known him for ages."

"Look, Susan, there's the boat we're going on," said Alvin stopping at one of the pretty bridges and pointing down the canal to where "Jason," one of the oldest, narrow canal barges, was moored.

"The 'Jason' was originally pulled by horses," owner Tony Hopkins told us, "but now, she is used

for pleasure trips up and down the canal and boasts an engine."

As we passed Brownings Island, overhung with weeping willows, it was alive with ducks, drakes and mallards.

"Come and help me feed the birds, Susan," Alvin shouted, producing a huge quantity of stale bread.

So, hanging precariously over the side of the boat, they threw bread into the water to a gaggle of greedy, chattering birds.

Just then a crowd of canoeists came paddling past and Alvin told us of a time when he was posing for photographs in an Olympic class scull on the River Thames.

"The scull was only nine inches wide and, as I lifted the enormous oars, the boat turned over and I was in the water.

"It was absolute panic stations, with me struggling and trying to hold on to the boat and the oars, when thankfully my feet touched the river bottom. I realised then that the river was only about 4 feet deep and I'd been panicking for nothing."

After a good laugh, Susan suggested that they try

their hand at steering the boat.

Balancing their way gingerly along the side of the boat, they climbed up to the wheel and the "Jason" was under new management!

"Look to your life-belts down there," Susan giggled. "Here we go."

Feeling decidedly nervous at first, I had to admit that the pair steered well and, as we approached Regents Park Zoo, Susan pointed excitedly to some animals on one side of the canal and, to the beautiful aviary, designed by Lord Snowdon, on the other. But enough of birds, it was time for the landlubbers to swab the decks!

AS we floated on past beautiful gardens and trees with Tony once more at the helm, Alvin brought out his guitar and asked Susan what she would like him to sing for her.

And, with the strains of, " Good Love Can Never Die," we sailed on towards Camden Lock, where we would turn for our return journey.

" I've got a smalll guitar at home," Susan told Alvin, as he finished his song. " I once played chords with some other girls in a school Christmas concert. But I'd love to be able to play properly."

" Nothing easier," smiled Alvin, lifting Susan up to sit beside him; then proceeded to give her a lesson.

" I really will practise from now on," Susan promised.

Susan's dream day was coming to an end, but, before it did, she was quite determined to carry away one momento at least.

" Smile, please," she urged Alvin, pointing her camera towards him, and snapping away like a professional.

Signing Susan's autograph book, " To Susan with love from Alvin," came next and, when " Jason " arrived back at Little Venice, Alvin presented Susan with a pot of lovely flowers.

" I don't give bunches. I like to be different," he laughed. " And, whenever I'm appearing anywhere

near where you live, just phone and you can have complimentary tickets to see the show," Alvin added.

" Just wait until the girls at home hear about this," Susan grinned at me, delightedly.

But Susan's mates would have been even more envious if they could have seen Alvin drive her home, then give her a kiss and a big "Thank you for a lovely day " hug.

" It's been a wonderful day," Susan sighed contentedly, as we waved goodbye. " Alvin turned out to be even nicer than I ever imagined. And it really has been like a dream . . . come true."

M. J. SMITH

Low Down

On Leo

Date of birth: May 24, 1948.

Place of birth: Shoreham, Sussex.

Real name: Gerry Sayer.

Father's occupation: Hospital engineer.

Mother's occupation: Nurse.

Has elder sister, younger brother.

Raised in house in hospital grounds.

Quote: " Being small, I was the target for bullies at school. This didn't help my studies and I failed my 11-plus."

Did first singing in church choir at Steyning, Sussex.

Best school subject: Drawing and painting.

Quote: " I was a very mixed-up kid and always a dreamer."

Spent two years at Worthing Art College.

Quote: " I dreamed of being a clown.

First job: Commercial artist.

Music debut: Mouth organ player in blues band.

After move to London, busked in streets.

Quote: " I was terribly lonely in London and wrote poems which expressed my feelings."

Wrote novel " The Avenue"—had no faith in it—chucked it on fire.

Early singing with group called Patches. (Disc debut with them).

Personal facts: 5ft 4 ins. Eight stone. Brown hair and eyes.

Met manager Adam Faith—pop star of sixties—in 1972.

Adam persuaded him to go solo.

Began songwriting with David Courtney 1973.

Roger Daltrey of The Who used some of their songs—including the hit " Giving It All Away."

In 1974, Leo had hits with first single " The Show Must Go On" and first album " Silverbird."

Used ideas from novel on first album.

In 1973 married Janice—a library assistant from Worthing, Sussex.

He had met her through another musician.

Before marriage, Leo once lived on houseboat.

First home with Janice: flat shared with another couple.

Leo once hated his curly hair and used stuff to try and straighten it.

Name " Leo" suggested by Adam Faith's wife.

Her reason: his hair was a bit like a lion's mane.

Quote: " I used to get terribly embarrassed about being spotted. But now I wear success as naturally as I wear a sweater."

Leo's clown outfit—used when he was first famous—designed by Jan.

Late 1975, Leo and Jan moved into house by Thames at Richmond, Surrey—with their pet gerbils.

Leo's friends call him Lee.

In November, 1975, had operation to remove four infected wisdom teeth.

Quote: " In some ways it's really nice being small.

Likes doing complicated construction kits.

In March, 1977, did one-man song and dance show on BBC TV.

Quote: " To me, success is not being able to go to the laundrette or supermarket any more."

Believes in cat naps during day.

In October, 1977, cancelled London Palladium shows because of laryngitis.

Quote: " It's lovely when my mum and dad like my new album—and yet it also appeals to young fans."

Is keen photographer.

Quote: " I love performing in America but miss being able to get a good pot of tea."

Disc label: Chrysalis.

Likes pies from Fortnum & Mason, the West End store.

Quote: " My songs are little bits of my past coming up and hitting me in the face."

I Remember, I Remember
continued

BILL RICE
(FLINTLOCK)

" . . . having a giant teddy bear one Christmas. I suppose I must have been about four at the time and the teddy was about the same size as me, if not bigger. I called him Bruno, and I really loved him.

But eventually I got too old for him, and what was left of him was given to the Dr. Barnardo Home."

DAVID NICHOLSON
(BLUE)

" . . . going to school for the very first time. The teacher was very busy and spent the first hour or so rushing about trying to check up on everybody's name to make sure we were all there.

I can remember sitting in the corner with some other kids and we were having a whistling competition. It turned out that I was the only person in the entire class who couldn't whistle at all!! "

DENIECE WILLIAMS

" . . . being given a huge great brown teddy bear, who was two feet bigger than me! I dragged him around by his ears while my grandfather took photos of us.

He was a lovely bear, but I used to get so angry with him because my arms weren't long enough to go round him, so I couldn't hug him until I grew another foot taller! "

BRENDON

" . . . when I was a baby I'd just started to toddle and my father took me into the garden. I can remember falling over a couple of times and him saying something like " Can't you even manage to walk yet? "

PETE SPENCER
(SMOKIE)

" . . . having a nightmare about a Yorkshire Pudding! I was only a kid and I dreamt that I was running along the side of a hedge and there was this giant Yorkshire Pudding on the other side, chasing me!! "

JANIE

PART SIX

WAKING up next morning, none of them had dared to ask for newspapers. They were finally brought to life by the ringing of the telephone.

"Have you read it?" he crowed. "We couldn't have got more or better publicity if we'd paid for it!" He took a deep breath. "Spread right across the centre page of the Daily Star. We're made, I tell you! It'll put Spinning Jenny right where we belong!"

In a daze, the boys sent out for the morning papers.

And there was the story, just as Magnus had said.

It had been sheer luck for them that the journalists had happened to pick on the boy that the group had tried to rescue.

He'd given a glowing accurate report of Spinning Jenny's part in the trouble, and been backed up by several others, including the disc jockey from the disco who'd been close enough to confirm the story.

"Look at this," said Les, reaching the end of the page. "'Local Magistrate says we need more teenagers of Spinning Jenny's calibre. They have proved themselves to be good and useful citizens. Where they lead, others might do well to follow'."

"Crikey," breathed Andy, "who'd have thought it."

The opening of the boutique proved a huge success, with the crowd demanding and getting "Farewell Gipsy Lady," several times over. Janie felt quite hoarse by the time it was all finished.

She and Rich escaped back to the hotel for a coffee and found a message from Magnus waiting for them. They'd been booked for a 'Top of the Pops' appearance later that day.

Afterwards, when she thought about it, Janie could hardly recall that first appearance in front of the television cameras.

She remembered the heat of the lights and the closeness of the audience, dancing almost at her feet.

She remembered the gipsy hoop earrings all the girls wore, so much like her own. She remembered them swaying to Rich's drumming.

She didn't remember herself actually singing, actually appearing in front of them all. It was almost as if she were standing outside of her own body, looking down and watching what was happening.

Later, looking at themselves on the screen, they were all pleased with the result. Most of all, Magnus. He'd come round to celebrate with them, bringing a sheaf of papers.

"Best news of the day," he told them. "Got a big tour lined up for you. Supporting a couple of the really top outfits," He grinned. "One day the tables may be turned and they may even be supporting you! You never know. Anyway, this'll do for a start. A whole month of engagements, nationwide."

He sat on the edge of the table, rubbing his plump hands, beaming widely at them all. "Few days rest first, eh? Take a bit of a holiday. You deserve it."

Janie and Rich went to stay with Janie's parents. Now, wherever they went, they were accepted as a twosome. And that was the way both of them wanted it to be.

"Doesn't seem all that long ago since I used to follow Spinning Jenny round," Janie murmured to Rich as they walked through the old familiar streets on their last night. "I used to dream of singing with the group. I never ever thought it would all come true."

Even now, she thought silently to herself, I still feel the bubble will burst and I'll be back at the beginning, just one of the watchers, one of the fans. "Farewell Gipsy Lady" will slip down the charts, and people will forget Spinning Jenny ever existed.

But she was wrong.

Back in town with the rest of the group, preparing for the big tour, she nearly jumped out of her skin when Rich came flying in, breathless with excitement, waving a paper.

"We're Number One!" he finally managed to get out. "We've made it! We're Number One in the Top Ten charts!" He grabbed Janie and whirled her round. "And just listen to what it says about my girl: 'Unknown singer makes the grade and, given the voice plus the personality, proves it can still be done. Watch Janie and Spinning Jenny. It'll be a long long time before we hear the last of them'."

A long long time.

Janie clung tightly to Rich.

She'd got all she'd ever wanted. She was the luckiest girl in the whole world.

And she'd never, ever forget it . . . no matter what the future held.

THE END